Animal Experiments:
Simple Truths

Dr Vernon Coleman

Ethics   170.0

Books by Vernon Coleman include:

The Medicine Men (1975)
Paper Doctors (1976)
Stress Control (1978)
The Home Pharmacy (1980)
Aspirin or Ambulance (1980)
Face Values (1981)
The Good Medicine Guide (1982)
Bodypower (1983)
Thomas Winsden's Cricketing Almanack (1983)
Diary of a Cricket Lover (1984)
Bodysense (1984)
Life Without Tranquillisers (1985)
The Story Of Medicine (1985, 1998)
Mindpower (1986)
Addicts and Addictions (1986)
Dr Vernon Coleman's Guide To Alternative Medicine (1988)
Stress Management Techniques (1988)
Know Yourself (1988)
The Health Scandal (1988)
The 20 Minute Health Check (1989)
Sex For Everyone (1989)
Mind Over Body (1989)
Eat Green Lose Weight (1990)
How To Overcome Toxic Stress (1990)
Why Animal Experiments Must Stop (1991)
The Drugs Myth (1992)
Complete Guide To Sex (1993)
How to Conquer Backache (1993)
How to Conquer Pain (1993)
Betrayal of Trust (1994)
Know Your Drugs (1994, 1997)
Food for Thought (1994, revised edition 2000)
The Traditional Home Doctor (1994)
People Watching (1995)
Relief from IBS (1995)
The Parent's Handbook (1995)
Men in Dresses (1996)

Power over Cancer (1996)
Crossdressing (1996)
High Blood Pressure (1996)
How to Conquer Arthritis (1996)
How To Stop Your Doctor Killing You (1996, revised edition 2003)
Fighting For Animals (1996)
Alice and Other Friends (1996)
Spiritpower (1997)
How To Publish Your Own Book (1999)
How To Relax and Overcome Stress (1999)
Animal Rights – Human Wrongs (1999)
Superbody (1999)
Complete Guide to Life (2000)
Strange But True (2000)
Daily Inspirations (2000)
Stomach Problems: Relief At Last (2001)
How To Overcome Guilt (2001)
How To Live Longer (2001)
Sex (2001)
We Love Cats (2002)
England Our England (2002)
Rogue Nation (2003)
People Push Bottles Up Peaceniks (2003)
The Cats' Own Annual (2003)
Confronting The Global Bully (2004)
Saving England (2004)
Why Everything Is Going To Get Worse Before It Gets Better (2004)
The Secret Lives of Cats (2004)
The Cat Basket (2005)
The Truth They Won't Tell You (And Don't Want You To Know)
    About The EU (2005)
Living in a Fascist Country (2006)
How To Protect and Preserve Your Freedom, Identity and Privacy (2006)
The Catholic's Handbook (2006)

novels
The Village Cricket Tour (1990)
The Bilbury Chronicles (1992)
Bilbury Grange (1993)

Mrs Caldicot's Cabbage War (1993)
Bilbury Revels (1994)
Deadline (1994)
The Man Who Inherited a Golf Course (1995)
Bilbury Pie (1995)
Bilbury Country (1996)
Second Innings (1999)
Around the Wicket (2000)
It's Never Too Late (2001)
Paris In My Springtime (2002)
Mrs Caldicot's Knickerbocker Glory (2003)
Too Many Clubs And Not Enough Balls (2005)
Tunnel (1980, 2005)

as Edward Vernon
Practice Makes Perfect (1977)
Practise What You Preach (1978)
Getting Into Practice (1979)
Aphrodisiacs – An Owner's Manual (1983)

with Alice
Alice's Diary (1989)
Alice's Adventures (1992)

with Donna Antoinette Coleman
How To Conquer Health Problems Between Ages 50 and 120 (2003)
Health Secrets Doctors Share With Their Families (2005)

Animal Experiments: Simple Truths

Dr Vernon Coleman

BLUE BOOKS

Published by Blue Books, Publishing House, Trinity Place, Barnstaple, Devon EX32 9HG, England.

This book is copyright. Enquiries should be addressed to the author c/o the publishers.

© Vernon Coleman 2006. The moral right of Vernon Coleman to be identified as the author of this work has been asserted in accordance with the Copyright, Designs and Patents Act 1988.

ISBN: 1 899726 51 9

A catalogue record for this book is available from the British Library.

Printed by Antony Rowe Ltd, Wiltshire

This book is dedicated to:

1. The countless millions of animals who have been caged without compassion, kept without dignity and tortured to death without reason.

2. The countless thousands of human patients who have died because they have been given treatments falsely marketed as safe on the basis of commercially expedient (but medically irrelevant) experiments performed on animals.

3. The thousands of campaigners who have fought frustration and injustice, suffered anger and tears and dedicated themselves to fighting an unequal battle against the ignorance, prejudice and greed of those who support animal experimentation.

4. And, of course, to my wife Donna Antoinette who cares and without whom this book would not be.

Preface

What's the real truth about animal experiments? Are they a reliable and essential way to assess new drugs and other new therapies? Do doctors think they are necessary? Are animal experiments necessary and justifiable, or are they indefensible and pointless? Are there better ways to test new drugs? Are those who campaign against vivisection simply terrorists who care little about animals but just hate people? Or are the defenders of vivisection intellectual terrorists, using blackmail to frighten the public into supporting their activities. Are animal experiments done because they enable drug companies to market drugs without doing proper testing?

The Government, the media and the establishment are all so committed to animal experimentation that they refuse point blank even to question the validity of what goes on in laboratories. For them there is no debate because there is no doubt.

But there is doubt.

And there must be debate.

The truth cannot be suppressed.

Many supporters of the anti-vivisection movement have, in the past, complained to me that they do not know what to say when vivisectors make specific medical or scientific claims about the value of the work they do.

I hope that this book will help anti-vivisectionists understand exactly what to say when faced with the arguments put forward (often with apparent scientific logic) by the vivisectors and those who defend vivisection. I have explained why so many people still regard vivisection as unjustified and I have carefully examined all the arguments put forward by vivisectors and those who support them.

Sadly, most of those who support vivisection (including politicians and journalists) have very little idea of what goes on in laboratories and have even less idea of the value of what goes on, often with taxpayers' money and always with Government authority.

Some allegedly independent commentators have undoubtedly been 'bought' by the pharmaceutical industry but many who blindly support animal experimentation do so because they have been told (quite dishonestly) that animal experiments are an essential part of medicine and that without such experiments we are all doomed.

Encouraged by the drug industry's spin-doctors, commentators and self-ordained experts tend to dismiss anyone who opposes vivisection as an animal-loving fruitcake; someone who loves animals more than people.

'If it's the life of a rat or the life of my child then my child gets my vote any day,' is a common piece of bluster from those who have found it easier to adopt prejudices than to study facts.

Animal Experiments: Simple Truths is a cool and dispassionate look at vivisection and a scientific appraisal of the value of animal experiments. Read this book and you can make up your own mind about whether such experiments save lives or are cruel, pointless and unnecessary.

I sincerely hope that this book helps to spread the truth.

In the end the truth will win.

Vernon Coleman May 2006

1

Here are nine basic facts about animal experiments:

1. Every thirty seconds vivisectors kill another thousand animals.

2. Vivisectors use cats, dogs, puppies, kittens, horses, sheep, rats, mice, guinea pigs, rabbits, monkeys, baboons and any other creature you can think of.

3. While waiting to be used in laboratory experiments animals are kept in solitary confinement in small cages. Alone and frightened they can hear the screams of the other animals being experimented upon.

4. Many of the animals used in laboratory experiments are pets which have been kidnapped, taken off the streets and sold to the vivisectors.

5. Animals used in experiments are tortured, blinded, burned, shot, injected and dissected. They have their eyes sewn up or their limbs broken. Chemicals are injected into their brains and their screams of anguish are coldly recorded. If an animal lives through this torture it will then be killed.

6. Three quarters of the experiments performed by vivisectors are done without any anaesthetic.

7. Most of the experimenters who torture and kill animals have no medical or veterinary training.

8. Most animal experiments are paid for with your money.

9. Animal experiments are now recognised to be of absolutely no value to patients or doctors or to anyone else. Animal experiments are performed by companies wanting to put new products onto the market without doing more expensive tests and by second-rate scientists wanting to acquire academic status the easy way.

2

Think of the animal you love most dearly. If he or she is close to you, reach out and touch him or her. Now, imagine your pet dog, cat or rabbit strapped – alive and alert – to the vivisector's laboratory bench. Imagine the vivisector approaching with scalpel raised. Imagine a tube implanted into your pet's brain and a scientist deliberately injecting an irritating chemical down the tube directly into your pet's brain. Imagine the scientist sitting back and waiting to see what happens. Within a minute or two your pet begins to shiver. The shivering is mild at first but it quickly becomes vigorous and widespread. Then your pet begins to cry; loud and pitiful cries. It begins breathing rapidly and salivating. Its ears twitch and its hair stands on end. It vomits, wets itself and empties its bowels. The white-coated, cold-blooded scientist who is watching all this dispassionately observes your pet's distress and carefully writes everything down in his notebook.

That is no fiction. It is real. It happens every day. In your name. With your money. And someone else's pet. Every 30 seconds that is exactly what happens to 1000 animals. It could happen to your pet if the vivisectors get hold of him or her.

3

Many of the drugs which doctors prescribe for human patients are known to cause cancer or other serious problems when given to animals.

Here's how it works: if a drug is given to an animal and the animal dies (or is made ill) the results of the test will be ignored. The drug will still be given to people on the grounds that people are different to animals and so the results of the tests on animals can be ignored. If, on the other hand, a drug is given to an animal, and the animal survives the experience, the drug company and its researchers will claim that this shows the drug to be safe.

The Government's advisers collude with this nonsense.

Nothing illustrates the nonsense of animal testing better than the fact that when the results of animal tests are commercially inconvenient they are ignored as irrelevant.

4

Those who abuse animals often argue that pro-animal campaigners do not care about people as much as animals. This is, of course, arrant non-sense. Just about everyone in history who has campaigned for people has also campaigned vigorously for animals. Abuse is abuse, whomsoever the victim may be. Abraham Lincoln, the 16th President of the USA who abolished slavery believed that animal rights were as important as human rights. William Wilberforce and Henry David Thoreau both fought for animals as well as people. Lord Shaftesbury, a social reformer who campaigned for free education and to stop children being employed in the mines, campaigned against animal abuse and for the total abolition of vivisection. Albert Einstein was a vegetarian who fought for animal rights. John Locke, the philosopher, believed in animal rights as well as human rights and wrote that if children were cruel to animals it would harden their hearts towards other humans. Dr Albert Schweitzer, the theologian who won the 1952 Nobel Peace Prize and is famed for his work in his African hospital was a vegetarian who believed in reverence for all forms of life. Buddha, who founded the religion named after him, taught that men should not hurt or kill any living creature. Charles Darwin believed that to love all living creatures was the most noble attribute in man. C.S.Lewis and Robert Browning both campaigned against vivisection. Gandhi, who led the Indian people to independence by non-violent means, was a vegetarian who believed that vivisection was the blackest of all black crimes committed against God. Voltaire, the French author, attacked the absurd Cartesian principle that animals were no more than machines. Mark Twain, the American humorist who supported many social reforms was a stern critic of all forms of animal abuse. Sir Isaac Newton believed that humanity should be extended to include animals. Jeremy Bentham, the philosopher and legal reformer believed that humanity should protect every creature which breathes. George Bernard Shaw, the Nobel Prize winning social reformer was a vegetarian who campaigned against all animal abuse including vivisection. The philosopher Arthur Schopenhauer wrote that 'compassion for animals is intimately connected with goodness of character; and it may be confidently asserted that he who is cruel to animals cannot be a good man.'

5

Here are some brief summaries of experiments conducted in recent years. As you read these summaries please remember that many of these experiments were conducted with money raised from taxpayers:

♦ Researchers blinded domestic tabby kittens by sewing up their conjunctivae and eyelids. The kittens were then placed in a special holder and horseradish peroxide was injected into their brains. The kittens were then killed.

♦ Three researchers conducted an experiment in which female hamsters were distracted with sunflower seeds so that their babies could be removed from the nest a few hours after birth. Under 'hypothermic anaesthesia' the baby hamsters had their left eyes removed. They were then returned to their mothers. The scientists used fifty-nine golden hamsters in this experiment and removed the left eyes from 'about half'. (The use of the word 'about' is the word used by the researchers; this will be no surprise to those who routinely study scientific papers written by vivisectors.)

♦ A researcher spent nine weeks forcing thirty-nine monkeys to run on a cylindrical treadmill known as an 'activity wheel'. If the monkeys failed to run for long enough they got an electric shock.

♦ Researchers gave ferrets a drug that made them vomit at intervals of between half a minute and five minutes. The researchers concluded that under some circumstances the ferrets did not stand up to vomit and that under the influence of a second drug their vomiting was less forceful.

♦ Three adult female cats were specially selected for an experiment because they were very trusting and docile. Wires from the cats' eyes were connected to a device held in place on the cats' skulls with self-tapping stainless steel screws. The cats were kept awake and their eye movements measured while their bodies were rotated and tilted and stimulated in other ways.

♦ Researchers separated young kittens from their mothers to see what effect this had. At the end of the experiment the scientists concluded that separated kittens cried more than those who remained in close contact with their mothers. The scientists added that the crying seemed to denote stress.

♦ Two researchers conducted a series of experiments designed to make baby monkeys depressed. To begin with they created a cloth, surrogate mother which could be triggered to blow out high-pressure compressed air. When the baby monkey went to give its fake mum a hug the researcher would press a button and try to blast the baby monkey away. When this did not work and the baby monkey merely clung on tighter, the researchers built a surrogate monster mother that was designed to rock so violently that the baby's 'head and teeth would rattle'. Again, the baby monkey just clung on tightly. The third monster had a wire frame built into its body. The frame was designed to throw the baby away from it. This worked to a certain extent – in that it did successfully separate the baby from its fake mother – but the baby monkey just picked itself up and went back to its fake mother immediately afterwards. In a final attempt to alienate, terrify, and thus depress the baby monkey the researchers built a 'porcupine' mother from which, at the press of a remote switch, sharp brass spikes would leap out. Once again the experiment was a failure for although the baby monkey was upset by the spikes it simply waited until the spikes had been withdrawn before returning to its fake mother.

- The same researchers built a 'well of despair' for monkeys. They built a vertical chamber with stainless steel sides and a rounded bottom and put young monkeys in it for weeks at a time. On this occasion the researchers were successful. The monkeys eventually sat huddled at the bottom of the chamber looking very depressed.

- Scientists pushed fine polythene tubes into rats' brains. They then put balloons into the rats' brains and blew them up. They found that all the rats suffered brain damage but that the smaller balloons did not produce as much damage as the big balloons.

- Four research scientists surgically joined together 224 individual rats to make 112 sets of 'fake' Siamese twins.

- Rats' tails were immersed in hot water so that researchers could study pain in rats.

- Ten beagle dogs were deliberately given stomach ulcers.

- Balloons made from condoms were pushed into dogs' stomachs through metal tubes and then filled with water. During the experiment the dogs, which were hung in slings, were kept awake.

- The livers, kidneys and lungs of Guernsey calves were deliberately damaged to see how this affected the way the animals responded to drugs. The researchers concluded that animals with damaged organs sometimes get more unpleasant side effects when they take drugs.

- Six monkeys were given a drug so that they would develop Parkinson's disease. They were then given the drug which is commonly used to treat Parkinson's disease in humans. When the monkeys' symptoms improved they were killed.

- Cuts were made in the bodies of pregnant rats, and metal screws cooled in liquid nitrogen were held against the developing heads of the baby rats developing inside them. The baby rats were later killed and their brains removed so that the amount of damage could be assessed.

- Two researchers found that if they breathed heavily on ants as they came out of their nest early in the morning the ants panicked.

- Three research workers shot around twenty monkeys just above the eye and then watched to see how long it took them to die. One monkey survived for over two and a half hours.

- A psychologist removed a monkey's visual cortex and then kept the blinded monkey for six years so that she could study her behaviour.

- Researchers have kept the brains of animals alive outside their bodies and have transplanted the heads of monkeys onto the bodies of other animals.

- A researcher gave a pair of rats a total of 15,000 electric shocks in seven and a half hours. Later the researcher heated the cage floor so that the rats inside jumped about, licking their feet, as the floor got hotter and hotter.

- Researchers clipped the hair from forty beagle puppies. They then put kerosene-soaked gauze onto the beagles' naked bodies and set fire to the gauze.

- Over thirty baboons were killed in forty mile an hour fake car crashes. A number of monkeys were killed when their skulls were hit with a hammering device. The experimenters showed that animals would be endangered if they drove cars into walls at forty miles an hour.

- Three polar bears were made to swim through a tank filled with crude oil and water. When the oil coated their fur the bears tried to lick themselves clean. They swallowed so much oil that they developed kidney failure and died. The conclusion was that polar bears should be kept away from oil slicks.

- Two scientists designed a drum rather like a tumble drier for traumatising alert, awake animals. The drum was made so that it turned over forty times a minute with the animal inside falling from one side to the other twice during each rotation. During a five minute experiment an animal inside the drum fell four hundred times. The animal's paws were taped together so that it could not break its own fall and interfere with the traumatising process. Animals traumatised in the drum suffered broken teeth, concussion, bleeding and bruising of the liver.

- One particularly eminent researcher discovered that if you stick mustard into the brain of a live, unanaethetised cat the animal will pant, salivate, leap up and down, miaow and try to bite its way through anything in reach. The researcher conducted variations on this experiment for around thirty years; injecting a variety of chemicals into the brains of live, unanaesthetised cats. He repeatedly discovered that cats shivered, salivated, retched, vomited and lost control of their bladders and bowels. He wrote many scientific papers and became one of Britain's most honoured scientists.

◆ Kittens were reared in complete darkness from the day they were born. As far as I could gather the conclusion the researcher came to at the end of his research was that kittens do not develop normally when they are reared in the dark.

6

Vivisectors say that animal experiments are useful because they enable scientists to check out observations made by clinicians.

But the truth is that animal experiments delay progress unnecessarily.

After doctors had observed that people who smoked tobacco seemed prone to developing cancer, animal experimenters spent years making dogs and monkeys smoke cigarettes in an attempt to establish a link between tobacco and cancer in animals. Much to the commercial profit of the tobacco companies this proved extremely difficult and doctors and politicians were discouraged, by decades of vague and inconclusive results, from providing warnings about tobacco for many years.

As a result, millions of people died unnecessarily. And the tobacco firms made billions of pounds that would not have been made without the help provided by animal experiments.

7

Many frequently prescribed drugs are known to cause cancer or other serious disorders when given to animals.

The information which follows was taken from the individual data sheets produced by the relevant drug companies. Many of the drugs on the list below are extremely popular and are prescribed for millions of patients around the world.

It would seem to me logical to argue that if animal experiments are worth doing then, (unless the benefit of using a drug can be shown clearly to outweigh the potential hazard), all these drugs should be taken off the market immediately – whereas if these drugs are considered safe for human patients then there is no point in continuing with animal experiments.

The prescription drugs on the following list have been marketed and passed as safe for humans but may increase the risk of tumours or cancer when given to animals. This list is by no means complete. There is more information about these drugs, and other drugs known to cause problems when given to animals, on my website www.vernoncoleman.com

Aldactide	Dianette	Ortho Dienoestrol Cream
Androcur	Dolmatil	Pharmorubicin
Apresoline	Farlutal	Retin-A products
Atromid-S	Grisovin	Retrovir
Bezalip	Hytrin	Roaccutane
BiCNU	Lasilactone	Spiroctan
Calcitare	Lopid	Sulpitil
Chendol	Losec	Tegretol
Chenofalk	Mithracin	Ursofalk
Cyprostat	Nolvadex	Zavedos
Depo-Provera	Normax	
Destolit	Novantrone	

It is quite clear that drug companies, the medical establishment and the Government must know that animal experiments are worthless. They defend the fiction – that animal experiments are of value – because of the vast financial benefits to the industry.

The key question (which vivisectors and their supporters can never answer) is: Why test on animals if you're going to ignore the results when they are inconvenient?

8

A few years ago the big cosmetic companies were all saying that they couldn't manage to make safe products without performing animal experiments.

Today, more and more cosmetic companies are publicly boasting that they no longer test their products on animals.

What happened?

9

Vivisectors say that new processes such as cell and tissue cultures are inadequate and that whole living organisms are essential for proper tests.

The truth is that cell cultures have been available for over a century and are extremely effective for testing new substances. In organ cultures small pieces of whole organs can be kept alive while enzyme and support systems are maintained.

It is true that whole organisms are necessary before conclusions about the efficacy and safety of a treatment can be reached but this requires human patients not animals.

10

Vivisectors claim that many drugs which have been tested on animals are useful and, with a staggering lack of logic, argue that this proves that animal tests are essential.

The truth is that just because scientists perform experiments on animals it does not follow that animal experiments are essential or even useful.

Most experimenters wear white coats and drink coffee. But that doesn't mean that the white coats and coffee are essential for the development of new drugs. In practice, the animal experiments, the white coats and the coffee are all as relevant (and as irrelevant) as each other.

Medical progress continues despite — and definitely not because of — animal research.

11

Vivisectors admit that animal tests can be misleading but argue that this is a reason for doing more experiments on animals. The truth is that more tests would simply mean more unreliable results, more confusion and more unnecessary deaths. Many useful drugs cause problems in some animals but not in others. It is impossible for anyone to know which tests to take notice of and which to ignore.

12

The vivisectors say that drug companies have to do animal tests to defend themselves against possible charges of negligence.

But, the truth is, in court expert witnesses called by drug companies have testified that data from animal experiments cannot be extrapolated safely to patients.

13

Vivisectors claim that vivisection is backed by hundreds of scientists who argue that animal experiments are essential and should continue. The truth is that a large proportion of the scientists who support vivisection earn their living doing animal experiments. They stand to lose everything – including income and reputation – if animal experiments are stopped.

And many of the rest who support animal experiments have received money, fees or payments in kind from drug companies. Most truly independent scientists, and the vast majority of qualified and practising doctors, are vigorously opposed to animal experiments.

14

Vivisection is a huge business. Apart from the grants, fat salaries and expense accounts received by the scientists who actually do the animal experiments, there are many large and profitable industries supplying animals, cages and restraints. Individual mice, genetically designed to develop cancer or some other disease, can cost huge sums of money. Primates cost tens of thousands of dollars each because they have to be captured in the wild. (The cost of obtaining animals is increased by the fact that many die while being shipped to laboratories.)

15

Animal tests used to assess possible carcinogenic substances are misleading because they are based on inaccurate ideas about how cancer develops and about the degree to which data gained from high doses of chemicals can reveal anything about the effects of low doses. The original theory was that if substances damage the DNA then they will cause cancer. But in some tests cancer develops because high doses of chemicals kill cells, provoking cell division which increases the risk of cancer.

According to animal tests coffee, tomato puree, peanut butter and alcoholic drinks all appear to be stuffed with naturally occurring carcinogens – up to 200 times as dangerous as the carcinogens in some banned chemicals.

The most absurd evidence of the futility of animal tests is surely the fact that tobacco smoke has been cleared of causing cancer in standard tests on rats. Rats can also consume vast quantities of alcohol without suffering any liver damage.

Only seven out of 19 known carcinogens were properly identified using the standard National Cancer Institute animal testing protocol in the USA. In vitro testing – using cell, tissue and organ cultures, is more sensitive, more accurate and less expensive.

16

Vivisectors don't take much, if any, notice of the age or sex of the animals they use. They claim that it doesn't matter whether they use puppies or dogs, young rats or old rats, female cats or male cats.

But the age and sex of humans matter a great deal when drugs are being used. For example, when the drug Opren – marketed for the treatment of arthritis – was originally tested on human beings it was not tested sufficiently on old people. But it was subsequently found that the drug had a much more dangerous reaction when given to elderly patients.

The age and sex of animals matter a lot too. Old rats are far more likely to get cancer than young ones and there are many other vital differences in the way members of the same species react. Female rats are usually more sensitive to toxicity than male rats.

I wonder how many of the researchers who realise this deliberately choose to use young male rats when testing a new drug – knowing that in this way they will be more likely to show that the drug is safe.

Another example of variations within a species is given by chimpanzees. Experiments on chimpanzees invariably use chimpanzees of differing ages despite the fact that there are enormous differences between immature and mature animals in physiological, anatomical, psychological and sexual terms.

17

Vivisectors are committed to defending what they do because if they admit that they were wrong to do experiments on animals they will expose themselves to ridicule and contempt and will have to admit that all the work they had done in the past has been useless.

Thousands of drugs which were launched on the basis of animal tests would have to be withdrawn and re-tested. Many would then be banned.

Animal researchers would find that their modest skills were worthless and their vast departments and huge drug industry pay-offs would be lost. Their apparent achievements would be devalued and it would be clear that they had wasted their lives.

I am not surprised that they are fighting hard. Meanwhile, animal experiments are quick and easy to do. It is possible to prove just about anything by using animals. And animal experiments lead to a steady supply of scientific papers which, in turn, lead to a profitable and almost endless supply of generous grants.

18

Vivisectors and their supporters try to claim the credit for just about every scientific discovery ever made. Whenever animals are used in research vivisectors claim that it was their work which made the breakthrough possible. Since animal experiments are so widespread vivisectors are able to claim responsibility for almost all advances in biomedical sciences. I wouldn't be surprised to hear vivisectors claim that animal experiments had led to the development of the motor car, television set and pop-up toaster.

19

Vivisectors claim that they are now introducing codes to ensure that animals are well looked after. But you can't have a code for vivisection any more than you can have a code for rape or murder.

20

Vivisectors claim that people who oppose vivisection would change their minds if they were ill or had sick relatives. Why should they? Animal experiments would not help and do, indeed, delay useful developments in the world of medicine.

21

The favourite fall back argument of people who do experiments on animals is that the drugs and other therapies developed through animal experiments are useful for the treatment of sick animals. For example, those who breed animals for experiments sometimes claim that the animals they breed and sell are used in experiments which will eventually help other animals.

But it is absurd to argue that it is acceptable to sew up the eyelids of perfectly healthy kittens, or to deliberately try to make monkeys depressed in order to treat another animal.

What sort of logic is there in torturing and killing animals to find treatments for other animals?

There is no need to breed cats in cages in order to do the experimental work that will help put new drugs on the market.

You don't have to torture human beings to find treatments for human beings and you don't have to torture cats to find treatments for cats.

There are many drugs on the market for human beings but as far as I am aware there are, as yet, no special farms in existence where human beings are bred and kept in cages so that they can be used in drug development.

22

Vivisectors claim that genetic experiments on animals are likely to lead to tremendous advances in medicine. But the truth is that three of the first 'developments' produced by genetic engineers were: a form of pest resistant tobacco plant, a type of calf so big that it needed to be delivered by caesarean section and a hybrid goat-sheep. The value and morality of genetic experiments still need to be debated but one thing is certain: genetic experiments on animals will never be relevant or justifiable.

23

Vivisectors say that animals have poorly-developed intellects when compared to human beings and can therefore be used in experiments without any fear. But a one-year-old year cat is more rational and sensible than a six-week-old baby.

24

Vivisectors sometimes argue that animals are very similar to human beings and are, therefore, suitable for experiments. But if animals are very similar to human beings why are we doing experiments on them? Surely such experiments must be ethically indefensible?

25

The abuse of animals in the name of science, performed by vivisectors in laboratories, may appear to be solely an abuse of animals. But since the end result of such experiments is the production, marketing and prescribing of drugs which are unsafe for human use, millions of people suffer (and many die) as a direct result of our reliance on animal experiments.

26

The Home Office in Britain has admitted that it has never conducted an evaluation of whether or not animal experiments benefit human medicine, nor has it ever assessed independent studies made by others, even though officials and politicians know that studies exist which show that animal experiments are ethically indefensible and completely without scientific or medical merit.

27

In its 1997 pre-election campaign, Britain's New Labour party made a number of promises on animal issues.

Most of these were quickly broken and forgotten.

One of the most significant promises was a clear commitment to hold a Royal Commission to assess the value of animal experimentation.

Way back in 1997, party leader Tony Blair and his colleagues were desperate to get votes from anyone. They made firm, clear promises to animal rights campaigners. And there is no doubt that the promise to have a Royal Commission (made in direct response to letters I wrote to Blair) won New Labour thousands of votes.

Elliot Morley MP, writing to me on behalf of Tony Blair on 10th December 1996, said: 'Labour is committed to seeing a reduction and the eventual end of animal experiments. We recognise that there is a debate on how essential animals are for developing life-saving drugs and treatment. For that reason we are proposing a Royal Commission to investigate the claims that animals need to be used and to recommend on alternatives.'

As soon as the 1997 election was won, Labour suddenly and conveniently 'forgot' the promise to consider a ban on vivisection. They decided that there wasn't need for a Royal Commission after all.

Yet again animals and animal lovers had been betrayed.

28

All great movements go through three stages: ridicule, discussion and, finally, adoption. Those who promote and benefit from vivisection have so far successfully managed to ensure that the anti-vivisection movement has remained in the first of these stages for many decades.

29

Most people are opposed to vivisection. But successive Governments have consistently used public money to support vivisection and to oppose anti-vivisectionists.

30

Vivisectors invariably claim that animals are properly anaesthetised during painful or uncomfortable experiments. This is a lie. Approximately three quarters of all experiments on animals are conducted without any anaesthetic at all. Even when anaesthetics are used the evidence shows that they are often inadequate. It is rare for a scientist experimenting on animals to have a properly trained anaesthetist present during a procedure and there is no doubt that many of those who have licences to experiment on animals understand little or nothing about how anaesthetics need to be given. As a result of this ignorance animals may be paralysed but not anaesthetised with the result that although they keep still they can still feel pain.

31

'Despite the lack of any systematic evidence for its effectiveness, basic animal research in the United Kingdom receives much more funding than clinical research.'

British Medical Journal

32

A few generations ago the legal status of a black person in America was roughly similar to that of a field of corn.

Future generations will hold vivisectors and their supporters with the same contempt as we now hold racists.

33

Vivisection supporters have been quite unable to find one patient whose life has been saved by animal experiments.

A couple of years ago I offered to give £250,000 to the first vivisector or vivisection supporter who could find one patient whose life had been saved as a direct result of animal experiments. The offer was widely and repeatedly publicised in the national press, in magazines and on the

Internet. But not one person came forward to claim the £250,000.

They couldn't.

Despite a desperate search vivisectors and their supporters have failed to find one patient, anywhere in the world, whose life has been saved by animal experiments.

I think it is safe to assume from this that even the vivisectors now know that no lives have been saved as a result of animal experiments.

34

In the *Journal of the Royal Society of Medicine* I found the following three scientific papers:

A) EFFECTS OF VIBRATION, NOISE AND RESTRAINT ON HEART RATE, BLOOD PRESSURE AND RENAL BLOOD FLOW IN THE PIG.

If you happen to be a pig operating a road drill this research work was probably useful. Otherwise I fail to see its significance.

B) EXERCISE IN NON-MAMMALIAN VERTEBRATES: A REVIEW

Here's the final sentence of the author's conclusions: 'Because of their oxygen-conserving response that can be brought into operation when under water, tufted ducks can vary their heart rate by a factor of twenty or more, depending on whether they are flying or whether they are trapped under water.'

C) EFFECT OF EXPERIMENTAL HYPOTHYROIDISM ON HEARING IN ADULT GUINEA PIGS

I suppose this paper might be of significance if you happen to be a deaf guinea pig with a thyroid problem.

35

Supporters of vivisection claim that diabetics owe their lives to animal experimentation. This is yet another myth created (and perpetuated) by those who want animal experiments to continue.

The truth is that the first link between the pancreas gland and diabetes was established in 1788 without any experiments being done on animals. And it was 22 years before that – in 1766 – that another doctor showed that the urine of diabetics was loaded with sugar (again, without animal experiments).

Throughout the 19th century progress in the investigation and treatment of diabetes was delayed while scientists wasted time performing useless animal experiments, trying to create diabetes in animals by destroying their pancreas glands. If vivisection had been banned two centuries ago diabetics would have benefited enormously and we would know a great deal more about diabetes today.

History shows that progress in medicine is usually made by observant clinicians and never by white-coated sadists torturing animals in laboratories. The medical evidence clearly shows that vivisectionists are responsible for the deaths of thousands of humans as well as animals.

36

Many of those who advocate or defend animal experimentation claim that animals must be used before drugs or cosmetics can be put onto the market. Vivisectors – many of whom work for drug and cosmetic companies – often claim that they only do experiments because they are forced to do so by law. Many independent commentators and anti-vivisection supporters have been taken in by these claims which are simply not true. The Home Office in the United Kingdom has confirmed to me that there are no laws – in Britain or the European Economic Community – which require drug or cosmetic companies to perform animal experiments.

Baroness Denton of Wakefield CBE, former Parliamentary Under-Secretary of State for Consumer Affairs and Small Firms told me that: 'There is no European Community or United Kingdom law which states that drug and cosmetic companies have to test their products on animals.' And Charles Wardle MP, when Parliamentary Under Secretary of State at the Home Office, confirmed that: 'There is no European Community or United Kingdom law which states that drug companies have to test their products on animals.'

It is the regulators (civil servants) who demand that new drugs be tested on animals, though I suspect that they do this at the behest of the drug companies.

The absence of any law requiring drug or cosmetic companies to perform animal tests means:

a) No law will have to be repealed before animal experiments can be stopped.

b) Since it has now been proved that animal experiments are useless they can easily be stopped without parliamentary intervention.

37

Those who support vivisection claim that animal experiments have saved millions of lives. But the truth is that animal experiments are responsible for millions of deaths. Many dangerous and lethal drugs have been put onto the market as a result of animal tests. Nearly all the drugs which cause serious side effects were originally tested on animals and were passed as 'safe' for human consumption.

38

Vivisectors regard the laboratory cat's squeals of protest as of little more significance than the squeaking of a rusty door hinge or a stiff axle. They say that animals are merely 'things' which exist to be used by humankind. But anyone who has ever spent time with animals knows that although it is impossible for us to imagine precisely how animals do think, or what they think about, there cannot possibly be any doubt that they are capable of thought. Simple observations confirm that animals feel pain, grieve, mourn and can be driven mad by abuse. Each member of the animal kingdom is different, but that does not mean that cats are any less alive than Frenchmen or that dogs are any less deserving of our compassion than children. Even rats – perhaps the most despised of laboratory animals – are intelligent, alert and sociable animals. They can develop relationships with one another and with human beings and they quickly become bored and frustrated when imprisoned.

39

Researchers with a simple way of looking at the world will frequently argue that animals do not have any rights. When pushed they will explain that the sole purpose of animals is to make our lives easier. The furthest they will go towards accepting that animals deserve to be treated with respect is to say that human beings share a responsibility to ensure that animals are not subjected to unnecessary suffering. The word 'unnecessary' is, of course, impossible to define satisfactorily and very few active researchers will ever admit that any experiments have ever involved 'unnecessary' suffering. This is, of course, the same elitist talk that graced the dinner tables of the pre-Wilberforce slave traders and it is the same sort of talk that still graces the (invariably) well-stocked dinner tables of the exceptionally fortunate and heavily prejudiced.

People, the vivisectors claim, are the centre of the universe; all else revolves around us.

We, they argue arrogantly, are entitled to do as we wish with the rest of the world. They insist that if it were not for human beings animals would have no role to play on this earth. Animals, they say, exist solely to provide us with food, clothing and pleasure.

The primitive mind which practises such potent speciesism and sees humankind as the sole purpose of creation and the single reason for life is unlikely to be swayed by arguments which demand such subtle expressions of intelligence as reason, insight or humility.

40

Those who support vivisection are the new racists.

41

Vivisectors say that animal experiments are not illegal, so how can they be wrong? But who can accept such a narrow, selfish and unforgiving argument? I confess that when I hear this argument aired I feel overcome by weariness and despair. 'It is against the law to torture and maim human beings in the name of science but it is not against the law to do these things to animals, so where can be the objection?' say the vivisectors.

Who can possibly live with such an absurdly mechanistic approach to life? The truth is that what is legal is not necessarily moral, any more than what is moral is necessarily legal.

42

'The love for all living creatures,' wrote Charles Darwin, 'is the most noble attribute of man.'

43

A researcher who wishes to experiment upon a human being must first obtain that individual's consent. Without consent any act of vivisection on a human being would be an illegal assault. But how can a researcher obtain consent from a monkey when planning an experiment? We know that monkeys can understand one another and can communicate with some human beings. So what gives a researcher the moral right either to assume that a monkey has given consent or to assume that obtaining that monkey's consent is unnecessary?

44

Vivisectors say that animals do not matter because they cannot think. I first heard this argument on a television programme some years ago. The dark-suited scientist who put it forward made the statement as though it were an accepted fact and as though it excused any sort of barbarity. 'Animals can't think', he said bluntly, looking around him as though that settled that. 'What about babies?' asked a young man in the audience, whose hair was dyed bright green and who had a cluster of safety pins through his nose and ears. 'Can they think?' He paused and thought for a moment. 'And what about the mentally ill, the educationally subnormal and people suffering from senile dementia? What about the infirm and people who do not have the money or the power to defend their rights?' He was absolutely right and the scientist had no answer. The fact that animals cannot think (even if it were true) is no excuse at all for treating them without respect. But is it true that animals cannot think? Is there any good reason to believe that a baby monkey does not 'feel' when separated from its mother and family, placed in a drum and left there, alone, for several weeks at a time? Just because animals do not speak our language, do we have any right to assume that they are stupid? This is, indeed, the sort of argument once followed by the worst sort of colonial Englishman. 'The natives don't speak English and so they must be stupid', he would argue with enviable simplicity.

45

As anyone who has ever lived with a cat will confirm, it is nonsense to say that cats are incapable of thought. They are remarkably intelligent and emotional creatures. They can communicate with one another and with human beings very effectively. And they even have skills that we certainly do not seem to have. There are, for example, numerous accounts of cats finding their way home on journeys of several hundred miles. Cats whose owners have died will walk for miles — crossing motorways, rivers and railways and passing through cities and across fields — in order to be with other human beings whom they like. Without maps or compasses cats can make long, arduous journeys with startling skill.

46

Each animal sees the world in a different light. Animals are not like people, but they are not like rocks either. Cats think and behave like cats. Monkeys think and behave like monkeys. Dogs think and behave like dogs. Only when we have made the effort to understand how dogs think and behave will we understand the full extent of their suffering when they are used in laboratory experiments. All animals are different. Cats like eating freshly killed mice. Cows like eating grass. Monkeys use their tails to help them swing through trees. Rats are happy eating stuff that we would feel uncomfortable about stepping in. None of this gives us the right to torture them.

47

By observing animals carefully it is possible to decide what sort of life they like best and it is also possible to see that when given a choice animals will always choose the least distressing of all the available options. But the people who conduct animal experiments do not bother to find out what the animals they use are really like. They do not want to know that the animals they are using have the intelligence to make choices. They do not like to think that the animals they are keeping might prefer a different lifestyle. The truth is that the conditions in which laboratory animals are kept are crude, cruel and barbaric. The way in which animals are used and abused shows that those who perform animal experiments have never made the slightest effort to understand the creatures whose lives they regard so lightly. The final irony is that researchers frequently claim that they can make judgements about behavioural patterns or the toxicity of tested substances by making laboratory observations. In fact, these observations and judgements are worthless because the circumstances in which the animals are kept and tested are unnatural and quite divorced from reality.

48

Vivisectors say that it does not matter whether animals can think or not; we are stronger and more powerful than they are so we have the right to do as we like with them. Surprisingly (and rather frighteningly) this argument is put forward quite frequently and there seem to be a large number of vivisectors who believe that the strong have a moral right to do what they like with the weak. What those who favour this argument do not seem to realise is that the same argument can be applied with equal logic within the human race. So, if it is perfectly right and fair for humans to torture, maim and kill baboons because we are (in some ways) more powerful than they are, then it must, by their argument, be equally acceptable for the strongest and most powerful human beings to use the weakest humans for their own purposes. If it is morally acceptable for a researcher to use this argument to support experiments on dogs, what is there to stop the same argument being used to justify experiments on children, old people or the mentally or physically disadvantaged? Scientists who promote this argument might like to think carefully about their own status in our society. If the intellectually deprived and socially worthless are to be used in experiments, then the vivisectors themselves will be among the first to find themselves selected for painful deaths in the laboratory.

49

Although many scientists are prepared to excuse the foulest of deeds on the basis that they are searching for knowledge, very few, if any, scientists are prepared to conduct their experiments at their own expense or in their own time. The vast majority of scientific experiments are performed by extremely well-paid scientists working in well-equipped laboratories. Those members of the public who find animal experiments unacceptable should also be aware that the vast majority of these experiments are conducted with public money at a time when doctors and teachers seem to agree that public services are suffering from a lack of funding. I wonder how many animal experimenters would carry on with their work if, instead of getting fat salaries from public funds, they had to pay for their experiments themselves? I suggest that some scientists would suddenly find that they had something more important to do. In other words, many vivisectors are driven not by a genuine, overriding thirst for knowledge, but by simple, old-fashioned, financial greed.

50

Britain's Department of Health has been quite unable to produce any scientific papers or other evidence showing that animal experiments are reliable or useful. The Department of Health's total failure to justify the Government's policy on animal experiments appears not to embarrass Ministers or civil servants who seem content to support vivisection on the grounds that they do it and therefore it doesn't need justifying. The House of Lords Animal Procedures Committee sent me a collection of scientific papers which the Department of Health claimed provided evidence in support of vivisection. The papers did no such thing, as I demonstrated in a review written for the House of Lords. (My review of the papers submitted by the Department of Health appears on my website www.vernoncoleman.com).

51

The British Medical Association is, as one would expect it to be, a staunch supporter of animal experimentation. But this stance becomes difficult to understand when one studies the British Medical Association's book: *The BMA Guide to Living With Risk* in which readers are told that: 'if salt and sugar were being tested as potential food additives today, and if judgement of acceptability was to be based purely on the laboratory and animal testing, it is unlikely that either would be permitted for use in food.'

It is difficult to imagine a simpler or more damning indictment of animal experimentation than to admit that animal experiments are so unreliable that neither salt nor sugar (just two of many other commonly consumed substances which are known to cause serious problems when given to other members of the animal kingdom) would pass safety tests if they were tested on animals.

52

One of the favourite debating tricks of those who support animal experimentation is to select a convenient date sometime in the past, point to all the scientific developments that have taken place since that time and then argue that without animal experiments none of those things would have happened. The implication is that animal experiments are justified because without them human progress will be held back. This argument is to logic what marshmallows are to a balanced diet. It is illogical to argue that just because animal experiments took place they were relevant, necessary or productive. The truth is that animal experiments have held back progress rather than aided it. You might as well argue that because people have managed to run faster and jump higher since animal experiments were started, there is a link between the two. You could as easily and as sensibly claim that without experiments on monkeys, cats and dogs we would still be relying on the town crier. Vivisectors assume that the only scientists with any capacity for original thought are the ones who chop up live animals. This is clearly nonsense.

53

Traditionally, scientists try to justify the work they do by claiming that they are helping to save lives. They are ruthless in the way they exploit public fears and anxieties in their attempts to preserve their own careers. But such claims are easily defeated by the facts and more and more often scientists are having to abandon this line of defence. When they are cornered and are unable to defend their work on practical or medical grounds, scientists will often claim that their work is justified simply because it adds to the sum of human knowledge. The work justifies itself, they say, and does not need to have any practical purpose. It is probably as pointless to try to counter this claim with moral or ethical arguments as it would have been to try to dissuade Josef Mengele from his evil work by telling him that it was 'wrong'. Throughout history there have always been scientists who have claimed that the search for knowledge justifies any activity, however repugnant. Like the Nazi and Japanese scientists who experimented on human beings and were convinced that their work was justified, today's animal experimenters seem to believe that their work, however barbaric, is justified if it can be claimed that it adds to the storehouse of human knowledge.

Those who are convinced by this argument might like to ask themselves where, if ever, the line should be drawn. Does the pursuit of knowledge justify any activity? There are some scientists who would say that it does; and there is no shortage of evidence that even today there are doctors who are willing to perform hazardous experiments on human patients under their care – patients who have never been asked for their permission. Patients around the world are frequently given new and untried drugs so that doctors can find out what happens. Patients have been injected with cancer cells to see whether or not they develop cancer.

During the last few decades thousands of human patients have been subjected to experimental brain surgery.

Many scientists who perform and support animal experiments also support experiments on human beings and will argue that such experiments are justified either because they add to the sum of human knowledge or because they help doctors develop new types of treatment.

One American scientist recently pointed out that: 'a human life is nothing compared with a new fact ... the aim of science is the advancement of human knowledge at any sacrifice to human life'.

When another scientist was attacked for using people in a nursing home for an experiment, he replied that he could not very well use scientists for his experiments because they were too valuable.

54

Vivisectors prefer to experiment on tame domestic cats because such animals tend to be more trusting and less troublesome when being handled in the laboratory. It is for this reason that so many domestic cats go missing every year. Thousands are stolen by professional cat thieves and sold to vivisectors so that they can be used in laboratories where animal experiments are performed.

55

Supporters of vivisection point out that every year thousands of animals are put down because they are ill or have been abandoned and claim that it makes sense to use those animals instead of wasting them. What the scientists who favour this argument fail to realise is that there is a considerable difference between putting an animal to sleep painlessly and subjecting it to a series of painful, humiliating and degrading scientific procedures. If this argument were sustainable then it would also make sense to use dying, lonely or 'unwanted' human beings for experiments.

56

Those who defend vivisection seem to find logic difficult to come by. They claim that the results from animal experiments can be utilised in the prevention or treatment of diseases which affect human beings but that animals are so different from human beings that we do not have to worry about them suffering any sort of pain or distress. These two arguments do not fit comfortably together. If animals are similar enough to human beings for the results to be of value to clinicians then the thousands of barbaric experiments which are conducted every day are insupportable, inexcusable and unforgivable on moral and ethical grounds. On the other hand, if animals are so fundamentally different to human beings that they do not suffer during procedures which would clearly be terrifying and enormously painful for human beings then the results obtained must be valueless.

57

Four out of ten patients suffer unpleasant, severe or fatal side effects after taking prescription drugs. One in six patients in hospital is there because he or she has been injured by a doctor. Since therapies prescribed by doctors are tested on animals (and passed as safe for human use partly on the basis of those tests) it is fair to blame the high incidence of doctor-induced illness on the reliance on animal experiments by drug companies and others. The cost of all these side effects puts a great burden on health services. If animal tests were abandoned, and drugs were tested more effectively, people would be healthier and health care costs would be lower.

58

Animal researchers received a £100,000 grant to study how worms defecate. Other researchers, who received £160,000, found that monkeys were less stressed by repeated electric shocks if they had a companion nearby. A third group of researchers, who received a more modest but still substantial £71,000, found that male monkeys were more likely to get erections when there was a female monkey in heat nearby. Remember these experiments next time you are invited to put money into a tin labelled: 'For Medical Research'.

59

Those who perform and support animal experiments are so embarrassed and ashamed of what they do that they frequently use euphemisms to disguise their activities. It is quite common, for example, for experimenters to talk of animals 'taking part' in experiments and 'helping us with our research'. Vivisectors may even describe animals as 'preparations'. The word 'experiment' has been replaced by the word 'procedure', which is less evocative. Experimenters have their own language. Who, other than vivisectors, could argue that animals do not cry or moan or whimper in pain? Animals, they say, are merely 'vocalising'. When animals are finished with they are frequently 'sacrificed'.

- ◆ Here are just a few phrases vivisectors use (together with their meanings):
- ◆ major airway embarrassment = choking
- ◆ reacting to adverse stimulation with vigorous motor responses = trying to escape

- binocular deprivation = sewing the eyes up
- decapitation = head removal
- exhibiting lethal behaviour = dying
- startle reflex = flinching
- aversive electrical stimulation = electric shocks
- thermal injury = burn or scald
- vocalising or vocal response = crying or whimpering

60

Psychologists have shown that students and teachers are desensitised by doing laboratory work with animals. Students who perform experiments develop an inhumane approach which affects their work with human beings.

It is clear that no one intending to work with patients should ever be exposed to animal experimentation. Students forced to undertake animal experiments as part of their studies will become so hardened by the suffering and daily deaths that they will become permanently desensitised to suffering.

61

The provision of animals and equipment for laboratories where experiments are performed is big business. Here are some facts about the industry which supports vivisectors:

- One company invented a machine capable of hitting dogs' hind legs 225 times a minute.
- Another company offered for sale a treadmill with variable speed controls and an adjustable device for giving electric shocks. The deluxe model (which automatically monitors the time an animal spends on the treadmill and the number of electric shocks it is given) costs more.
- A mouse breeding firm sells genetically engineered mice which are virtually guaranteed to develop cancer within 90 days and to die soon afterwards.
- A maker of laboratory equipment devised an individual water dispenser programmed to deliver an electric shock each time an animal takes a drink from it. The aim is to make the animal so anxious that it eventually stops drinking. To heighten the efficiency of the device experimenters are advised to deprive animals of water for two days

before putting them into the tiny cage to which the water dispenser is attached.

62

There is a strong relationship between those who are cruel to animals and those who are cruel to humans. As the following list makes clear, the sort of people who abuse animals are likely to abuse humans too.

1. Peter Kurten (aka the Dusseldorf Monster), practised bestiality on dogs and murdered more than 50 human beings.

2. Luke Woodham, set fire to his own dog, stabbed his mother and killed two teenage girls.

3. David Berkowitz shot his neighbour's dog, poisoned his mother's parakeet and killed six people.

4. Patrick Sherrill stole local pets for his dog to attack and murdered 14 people.

5. Jack Bassenti buried puppies alive and raped and murdered people.

6. Edward Kemperer chopped up cats and killed his grandparents, his mother and seven other women.

7. Henry Lee Lucas killed animals and murdered his wife and mother.

8. Michael Cartier, who threw a kitten through a closed window and pulled a rabbit's legs out of its sockets when he was four-years-old, grew up to become a murderer.

9. Randy Roth used an industrial sander on a frog, taped a cat to a car engine and killed two wives.

10. Jeffrey Dahmer killed many animals and 17 men.

11. Dr Josef Mengele, the German concentration camp doctor known as the Angel of Death was feared by millions. He was probably the most notorious doctor who ever lived. He was a vivisector who conducted experiments on animals as well as people.

63

It is claimed that without animal experiments surgery would not have progressed as far as it has. This is nonsense. Surgical experiments on animals can be enormously misleading. Consider psychosurgery for example. The first leucotomies were performed in the 1930's when it was thought that the frontal lobes were the source of delusions in mental patients. American workers removed the frontal lobes of chimpanzees in 1935 and thought that the animals were more contented afterwards. Since then, on the basis of those animal experiments, thousands of patients have had their frontal lobes cut out and the destruction of various parts of the brain has been carried out for a wide range of physical and mental conditions including schizophrenia, depression, obsessional neurosis, anxiety, hysteria, eczema, asthma, chronic rheumatism, anorexia nervosa, ulcerative colitis, tuberculosis, hypertension, angina, cancer pain and drug side effects.

It is also worth remembering that it was Galen's work on pigs two thousand years ago which misled surgeons for centuries. Galen based his writings and lectures on experiments he had conducted on pigs. It is now generally agreed among medical historians that Galen's work held back medical progress for centuries until religious restrictions were withdrawn and doctors were able to cut up human cadavers and discover that there are enormous differences between the anatomy of the pig and the anatomy of the human being.

64

Vivisectors claim that surgeons need to practice on animals to learn their skills. But surgeons in most countries – Britain for example – learn all their skills on human patients and not on animals. Even the law recognises the absurdity of practising surgery on animals and surgeons must practise their skills on people. Most vivisectors are unqualified to perform human surgery. Differences in anatomy mean that operations performed on animals are of no value to surgeons.

65

Vivisectors say that without proper drug tests performed on animals, pregnant women would be at risk. But animal experiments don't protect pregnant women at all. Indeed, they encourage an entirely false sense of security. We need to encourage doctors and drug companies to watch for, report and take note of side effects in order to protect patients properly. If proper drug surveillance techniques had been available in the 1960's the problems caused by the drug thalidomide would have been picked up much earlier. We still don't have proper post marketing trials in place. And most of the side effects caused by drugs go unreported because doctors are too ignorant or too lazy to report them.

66

When human cancer cells are injected into animals the cancers produced are biologically different to the ones that occur in humans.

67

Vivisectors claim that animal experiments help them assess the effectiveness of new drugs designed for the treatment of mental illness. But animals do not noticeably suffer from the same mental disorders as human beings. How can researchers possibly know whether or not animals are suffering from delusions or hallucinations? Mice have been provoked into fighting by being given electric shocks and then calmed with tranquillisers – but what is the point of this?

Animal experiments also fail to produce any evidence of addiction. For example, when the benzodiazepines were first being tested on animals researchers reported that the drug tamed monkeys, dogs, lions and tigers. These tests were used to help encourage doctors to prescribe the benzodiazepine drugs for vast numbers of patients. But the tests did not indicate that the benzodiazepines would turn out to be among the most addictive of all modern drugs.

68

Animal experiments are popular with scientists, since they enable researchers to obtain results relatively quickly. It is very easy to do research and to get it published by using animals. It is much easier to do experiments with animals than with people. There are fewer rules to obey and when things go wrong there is less likely to be any trouble. Most university departments are ruled by a quest for grants rather than a quest for knowledge and the validity of research is insignificant. The only thing that matters to them is the number of papers published.

69

The vast majority of vivisectors are not medically qualified. Very few fully-qualified doctors perform experiments on animals.

70

An editorial in the *British Medical Journal* claimed that modern scientific papers are so badly written that 99% are invalid. Scientists rely on the fact that very few people will question their work. The same BMJ editorial also reported that 85% of medical procedures have never been properly tested – 'only about 15% of medical interventions are supported by solid scientific evidence.' We should be spending our limited resources on assessing existing therapies rather than performing pointless and misleading tests on animals.

71

Vivisectors claim that animal experimenters get personal pleasure from their work and should be allowed to continue with it for that reason.

72

There is now clear evidence that people who perform animal experiments are exposing themselves to danger. A report in the *Journal of the American Medical Association* described an outbreak of lymphocytic choriomeningitis among laboratory workers handling mice or mice tissues. There have been a number of sarcomas and lymphomas at the Institut Pasteur in Paris where a survey showed an increase in the number of deaths from cancers of the bone, pancreas and brain among laboratory workers. And a report in *The Lancet* mentioned malignant melanomas and cancers of the blood as well as an increased risk of cancers of the brain and nervous system and stomach among laboratory staff. Animal experiments should be stopped to prevent laboratory staff from deliberately exposing themselves to unacceptable hazards.

73

Animals used in laboratories are kept in terrible conditions. Time and time again evidence becomes available that animals are kept in deplorable circumstances. These poor conditions make the results the researchers obtain even more unreliable than they would otherwise be. Most of the committees and organisations which are (theoretically) designed to ensure that researchers look after the animals they use are manned by researchers or by people who support animal experiments. This is like allowing criminals to police our streets.

74

Vivisectors claim that animals cannot feel pain or suffer in the same way that human beings can – and therefore animal experiments are justified and justifiable. But all the available evidence shows that animals can feel pain and can suffer from stress. The prerequisites for pain reception are a central nervous system, a system of peripheral pain receptors and a series of neural connections between the receptors and the central nervous system. All vertebrate animals possess these three essentials and can undoubtedly feel pain.

75

The drug tamoxifen, widely used as a treatment for women with breast cancer, causes liver tumours in rats. (It also causes gonadal tumours in mice.) This evidence was regarded as bad news for rats but meaningless for women. So, if drug companies and drug regulatory authorities can ignore animal tests when it suits them (on the grounds that animals are different to people) what on earth can be the point in doing yet more tests on animals? Not that it is just in the area of drugs that differences exist. A recent *British Medical Journal* editorial reported that: 'animal studies have made it clear that there are considerable differences in the effects of vasectomy among species. Which, if any of these models applies to man is not known '

76

Research scientists working in America conducted a research project to find out what happened when rats' whiskers were shaved. During the experiment a technician shaved the rats' whiskers every day with a pair of small scissors. The researchers found that the rats' brains didn't develop properly. Should we assume from this research that men who shave their beards are intellectually inferior to men who don't?

77

Vivisectors claim that animal experiments help in the fight against cancer but the truth is that because animal tests can be misleading there is a real risk that such experiments may hold back medical progress. An extremely eminent academic concluded, after a long study of cancer experiments: 'It has fallen to my lot to have to make a general survey of cancer in all its aspects and I do not believe that anyone who does this with an open mind can come to any other conclusion than that to search for the cause or cure of cancer by means of experiments on lower animals is useless. Time and money are spent in vain.'

78

The links between chemicals, X-rays, certain foods and asbestos on the one hand, and different types of cancer on the other, were obtained after doctors had studied human patients – not cats, dogs or rabbits. Animal experiments, conducted subsequently, slowed down the speed with which these discoveries were applied and were, consequently, responsible for the deaths of millions of people.

79

Vivisectors say that animal experiments are helping doctors treat high blood pressure. But the animals used in laboratory experiments do not normally suffer from high blood pressure. Researchers can only give the animals high blood pressure by tying off brood vessels, by removing kidneys or by interfering with the animal's normal physiology or anatomy so much that any resemblance to normality is lost. Advances in the treatment of high blood pressure have come from clinical experiences.

80

Claims that animal experiments have helped in the treatment of arthritis are false. Laboratory animals do not normally suffer from arthritis. To test new drugs researchers inject the joints of animals with irritating chemicals to produce some inflammation at the ends of the bones. It is still not arthritis. Trying to find dietary answers for arthritis by giving animals different foodstuffs is even more absurd because people don't eat the same type of diet as animals.

81

Some independent observers have criticised those who oppose the use of animals in vivisection for failing to campaign on behalf of human volunteers who are used in testing new drugs. 'This proves that animal lovers are putting animals above humans,' thundered one newspaper columnist who didn't seem aware that the word 'volunteer' implies choice, something that is, of course, denied to the animals who are used in experiments. (The human volunteers who take part in drug testing are well-paid. They are, indeed, so well-rewarded that when national coverage was given to a test which went wrong the result was that, instead of a dearth of new human volunteers, those organising drug trials found themselves overwhelmed with would-be human guinea pigs.)

82

If you are uncertain about the nature of vivisection then try this simple exercise: imagine you are a guinea pig taking part in a sensitisation test for a new perfume.

First, scientists would shave a patch of your skin – removing every small hair – so that the perfume would make the best possible contact with your skin. Then they would put a large quantity of concentrated perfume onto your skin and leave it there. A plaster would be put over the test area to make sure that the perfume remained in the closest possible contact with your skin. You might be tied down to make sure that you didn't move about and disturb the experiment. Every few hours or so the test site would be inspected. And more of the concentrated perfume would be added until your skin went red and started to itch.

You would want to scratch but you wouldn't be able to. A thick dressing would be put over the test area and your hands would be tied to stop you interfering with the experiment. The itching would get worse and worse. But the scientists doing the experiment wouldn't give you anything to stop the itching. If they did they would mess up their results.

Even if you cried and begged for mercy they would ignore you. These scientists are trained to ignore such pleas. It is their job to cause suffering – and to record the consequences.

Gradually, the area of skin under test would become redder and redder. Eventually it would probably begin to blister. Fluids would ooze out of your skin and drip out from underneath your bandage. You would probably notice some blood oozing out as well. Before long your whole body would probably begin to react. You might start to wheeze and to have difficulty in breathing. Your skin would start to burn and to itch and your heart might well start to pound.

The aim of a sensitisation experiment is deliberately to induce an allergy response by giving so much of the test product that the body responds violently. You would feel ill. You would probably feel nauseated and you might start to vomit. Still, the scientists would refuse to give you any treatment in case the treatment interfered with the test. Instead they would simply write down your symptoms and make notes about the condition of your skin. When they had acquired enough information they would kill you.

83

The truth is that animals can help doctors save human patients. But through observation – not experimentation.

Many vertebrates – including monkeys, pigs and elephants, use plants as medicines as well as food. Sick animals seek out and eat plants which they know will help them; they eat some plants, they hold others in their mouths and they rub a third group onto their skin. Ethiopian baboons who are at risk of developing schistosomiasis eat fruits which are rich in a potent antischistosome drug. Chimpanzees in Tanzania use a herb which has a powerful antifungal, antibacterial and antinematode activity. If they just ate the herb it wouldn't work because the valuable compound would be destroyed by stomach acidity. So they hold the leaf in their mouths in the same way that angina patients are encouraged to hold glyceryl trinitrate in their mouths to expedite absorption. Kodiak bears apply a drug topically which helps to kill parasites. They scratch the root into their fur. European starlings combat parasitisation to their nests by fumigating incubating eggs. Howler monkeys use herbal medicines to control birth spacing and to determine the sex of their offspring. And on and on it goes.

We can learn an enormous amount by watching other animals.

But instead of watching these sensitive, intelligent and thoughtful creatures the vandals in white coats cage them, torture them and kill them with all the scientific sense of youthful hooligans tearing the wings off flies; they stick electrodes into their heads, sit them in metal boxes for weeks at a time to make them depressed, separate them from their families, sew up their eyes and inject chemicals into their brains while they are awake.

84

In a generation or so our descendants will look back at the vivisectors and wonder not just at the sort of people they were, but at the sort of people we were to let them do what they did.

85

I met a man who told me that his company did a lot of testing on rabbits. The scientists shaved the rabbits so that they could 'paint' chemicals onto bare skin to see what happened. To speed things up they started dipping the live and conscious rabbits into acid to burn off their fur.

The man I met told me that he and his colleagues complained that the noise of the screaming rabbits made it difficult for them to concentrate on their work.

The scientists responded by building sound-proofing around the animal laboratory so that the screams could not be heard.

86

The world's vivisectors torture and kill countless millions of animals every year.

Every thirty seconds these Mengele-think-alike pseudo-intellectual thugs get through around one thousand cats, dogs, puppies, guinea pigs, monkeys, baboons, chimpanzees, rabbits, hamsters, mice, rats and kittens.

They obviously need a constant supply of animals to satisfy their depraved needs.

They often obtain monkeys, chimpanzees and similar animals from countries where such animals breed naturally. In some countries animals of this type are treated like vermin and can be hunted, captured and sold with no restrictions.

Mice needed for experiments are often specially bred.

In some countries, animals are bought from zoos (when there is a surplus). Animals which have 'retired' from other work may end up in laboratories.

But finding enough dogs and cats can be difficult.

In America where there isn't quite as much secrecy about these things it is now known that vivisectors regularly torture and kill former family pets. Amazingly, around two million pets are stolen every year in the U.S.

In one part of New York over 10,000 dogs were reported missing in a single nine-month period. One bereaved pet owner searched for his missing dog and found him inside a research laboratory.

Animal theft is really big business. Vivisectors prefer working with pet dogs and cats because they are tame and trusting – and less likely to bite or scratch.

I firmly believe that petnapping goes on in other countries too. Tragically, I believe if your dog or cat goes out at night there is a real risk that he or she could be captured and sold to a laboratory. If a family pet has ever mysteriously disappeared it could have found its way into a viWeiWveisoctor's laboratory.

Vivisectors will stop at nothing to obtain the animals they need. They don't care about the law. They don't care about the fact that families may mourn the loss of their loved pet. All they care about is getting another fat grant and performing yet more useless and cruel experiments. Vivisection is a big, rich business which needs an endless supply of raw material. And the raw material they need could be your much-loved family pet.

Animal lovers who have lost pets should have the right to enter all laboratories at any time to search for missing animals.

Why should vivisectors be entitled to do their evil work in secret – behind locked gates?

87

Here are three case histories which show that animal experiments kill people:

1. Eight-year-old Samantha loved ballet dancing passionately. She wanted to be a ballet dancer when she grew up. But she never did grow up. Ten days before her ninth birthday she fell ill. Her ballet class was holding a public performance on the following Saturday and she desperately wanted to be well enough to appear so her mother took her along to see their family GP. Within 48 hours Samantha was dead: killed not by the illness but by the drug she'd been given. The drug had been tested but most of the early tests had been done on animals. These had not shown the side effect which killed Samantha.

2. Forty-four-year-old Robert failed a routine life assurance examination, carried out so that he could take out a new and larger mortgage on a house he and his wife had bought. He felt well but his doctor insisted on treating him. The drug he was given had been extensively tested on mice and rats. Unexpected side effects produced by the drug resulted in his death three weeks later.

3. Bill was in pain. Doctors recommended surgery. The surgeon he saw wanted to try out a new technique that had been tested on animals. Bill died three days after the operation. He developed problems and complications which had not occurred when the operation had been performed on animals.

All these human tragedies occurred as a direct result of animal experiments. In all these case histories the identifying facts have been changed to protect the privacy of the families concerned. It isn't only animals who suffer from 'animal testing'. People suffer too.

Remember: no animal experiment has ever saved a human life, but animal experiments have resulted in many human deaths.

88

'...man and the higher animals, especially the primates, all have the same senses, intuitions, and sensations, similar passions, affections, and emotions, even the more complex ones such as jealousy, suspicion, emulation, gratitude and magnanimity; they practise deceit and are revengeful; they are sometimes susceptible to ridicule, and even have a sense of humour; they feel wonder and curiosity; they possess the same faculties of imitation, attention, deliberation, choice, memory, imagination, the association of ideas, and reason though in very different degrees.'

Charles Darwin

89

During 1989, 1990 and 1991 several scientific papers written about experiments involving dogs were published by scientists working for the Imperial Cancer Research Fund. For one experiment 60 male beagle puppies were anaesthetised and then bled to death.

The Imperial Cancer Research Fund (ICRF) claimed that the dog experiments were done because there were fears that a drug might cause problems in people. They told me that 'the FDA requested investigations of the mechanisms of hyperplasia associated with high doses of misoprostol'.

One of the papers published by the ICRF scientists ended: 'In conclusion, misoprostol effectively elicits a hyperplastic response in the gastric mucosa...'. The drug company making misoprostol told doctors: 'Cytotec (misoprostol) in multiples of the recommended therapeutic dose in animals has produced gastric mucosal hyperplasia...In patients, histological examination of the gastric biopsies taken before and after treatment with misoprostol after up to one year's duration have shown no adverse tissue response attributable to misoprostol.'

In other words the scientists from the ICRF showed that the drug produced hyperplasia in dogs but the drug company still sold the drug for human use and stated that human patients did not respond in the same way. The authorities were clearly happy that the drug was safe for human use, and ignored the animal experiments.

90

A BBC producer refused to broadcast an interview in which I had described the experiments performed by the Imperial Cancer Research Fund. In the interview I had said that the experiments had involved the deaths of a number of dogs.

'I'm not using your interview. They didn't use dogs at all,' the indignant BBC producer told me after talking to the people who had done the experiments.

'I have copies of the scientific papers which described the work,' I insisted. 'And according to the papers they used dogs.'

'No, they didn't,' insisted the producer, now almost incoherent with rage. 'I've been assured that they only used pieces of dogs – organs and tissues and things.'

The producer steadfastly refused to accept that you can't use bits of a dog without using or killing the dog. To this day I think the producer believed that the experimenters had simply tottered into Sainsbury's and bought a bag of assorted dog bits.

91

Those who campaign against animal experiments are routinely and variously condemned as mindless thugs, members of organised crime groups or dangerous terrorists who care more for animals than for people and who regularly menace and kill innocent laboratory workers. Those who campaign against vivisection are, claim the politicians, a serious threat to the nation's economy and the biggest threat to the nation's security. Vast numbers of new laws have been introduced in order to control the threat to a huge multi billion dollar industry. Whenever there is a demonstration against vivisection there will be a huge and intimidating police presence. People who think they live in a free, democratic country have never been on an animal rights march or attended a demonstration. In my book *Animal Rights Human Wrongs* I published first-hand reports from innocent people who had experienced police brutality in modern Britain.

On one occasion, when I was due to speak at an open air animal rights rally opposing vivisection, the Home Secretary and the police effectively shut me up by introducing a temporary law preventing me, or anyone else, travelling to the site of the rally. (When the rally was rearranged and the Home Secretary and police failed to ban my second attempt to speak they used a less subtle approach. A helicopter hovered right above the stage where I was speaking so that the noise would drown what I was saying.)

The truth is that no one involved in animal experimentation has ever been killed or seriously injured by campaigners opposed to vivisection. No one.

On the other hand three pro-animal campaigners have been killed in recent years. And hundreds of others have been physically manhandled, threatened or beaten up by the police or by those supporting vivisection.

92

Here are ten genuine discoveries made by scientists experimenting on animals. After details of each experiment I have included a short note explaining how the research may help you and your family.

1. Baby monkeys get terribly upset when they are parted from their mothers and kept in solitary confinement in steel containers for long periods. (Shows that school children should not be kept in solitary confinement in steel containers.)

2. Putting balloons inside animals' brains and blowing up the balloons causes brain damage. The bigger the balloon the greater the brain damage. (Clearly shows that children should not be allowed to blow up balloons inside each other's brains. And that if they must do this they should use small balloons.)

3. Rabbits' eyes go red and become sore and irritated when they are deliberately filled with toxic chemicals. (Suggests that you should not be surprised if your eyes hurt if you drop toxic chemicals into them).

4. Dogs die if they are forced to eat large quantities of soap. (Clear evidence that eating large quantities of soap is unwise.)

5. Live pigs suffer severe burns when they are exposed to naked flames. (Shows that if you want to avoid severe burns you should keep your distance from naked flames.)

6. If you shoot cats in the head they cry and scream a great deal, bleed

a lot and then eventually die. (Suggests that shooting people in the head may be painful, noisy and messy.)

7. If you deprive guinea pigs of water for long periods they become very dehydrated and eventually die. (Clear support for the belief that humans who don't drink fluids will die.)

8. Puppies and other animals die when you remove essential organs such as kidneys. (Suggests that it is unwise to allow anyone to remove your kidneys.)

9. Cats get very upset if you drill holes in their brains and then squirt chemicals into the holes. (Shows that drilling holes in people's brains and then filling the holes with chemicals is anti-social.)

10. Monkeys die when deliberately infected with bugs which cause fatal diseases in monkeys. (Shows that scientists who perform experiments on animals are mad psychopaths'.)

93

Why should we consider it a crime to torture a man to death – but at the same time support a government which gives public money to support a vivisector who tortures a monkey to death?

Where is the justice or the logic in it?

There is none.

94

For decades successive Governments have ignored calls for an independent investigation into the value of vivisection. As I explained earlier in this book, animal lovers were, in the mid 1990s, encouraged by promises made by New Labour. But the professionally deceitful Blair's promises proved to be as disposable as his promises on other issues. (Blair's adaptability inspired by expediency will be remembered as his most notable quality. It may be difficult to believe but before being made Prime Minister, he was fervently opposed both to the EU and to identity cards.) Animal lovers were duly betrayed. What happened? My guess is that when Blair got into power he realised that any Royal Commission must inevitably conclude that animal experiments are of no scientific or medical value and so he changed his mind. Blair's decision was doubtless inspired by his fear that there would be an exodus of large drug companies and that this would be devastating to the economy. In this, as in so many other things, Blair's reading of the situation was quite wrong. When a British Royal Commission found that animal experiments are of no value (as Blair feared it would) then the truth would spread worldwide and animal experiments would become illegal in all civilised countries. Drug companies would simply find another equally reliably ineffective way to test drugs.

Keen to ally himself with the large international drug companies Blair had, by 2006, declared himself an enthusiastic supporter of animal experiments.

95

If an independent Government enquiry would show that animal experiments are useful why won't they have one? Perhaps politicians and scientists know that an independent enquiry would expose vivisection as worthless.

96

Animals in laboratories are frequently abused. But those who do the abusing are rarely – if ever – punished. Even when lower courts find abusers guilty an appeal will usually reverse the decision. On one famous occasion a conviction was reversed on the grounds that human beings don't have the right to bring legal action against other humans on behalf of animals. If the animals don't initiate legal action themselves then no one can do it for them.

97

The authorities will do everything in their power to protect vivisectors and nothing to ensure that animals receive the extremely modest protection the law offers.

For example.

A vivisector went home and left a mouse with his head in a clamp. The mouse suffered terribly and was killed the next morning by a colleague.

Labour politician Jack Straw, when Home Secretary, knew (or had access to) the name of the callous vivisector responsible for this breach of the Protection of Animals Act 1911.

But although Straw did not deny that an offence had taken place he wouldn't reveal any details of the vivisector and he steadfastly refused to give the police the vivisector's name so that a prosecution could be considered. (Ironically, it was Straw who was one of the first politicians to accuse animal lovers of being terrorists.)

When I complained that the Home Secretary was protecting someone guilty of a crime, I was told by the Home Office that this was not an offence even though the vivisector was clearly in breach of the Protection of Animals Act 1911. Straw told me that he could decide whether or not a vivisector who broke the law – and was cruel to an animal – should be tried in court.

When I tried to get around Straw's determination to protect the vivisector from prosecution by reporting the offence to the police, I was told that without knowing the name of the vivisector nothing would be done. The police refused to ask the Home Office for the identity of the criminal.

I then asked the police to demand that Straw give them the information he had.

But the police refused.

A senior legal advisor for the police told me that not notifying the police of a crime is not an offence – unless there is treason or a conspiracy.

It is clear from this that vivisectors can break the law with impunity. And will be protected by the Government.

98

I wrote to all MPs about this case because I wanted to see how politicians felt about the fact that the Government was protecting a vivisector from prosecution.

Here are quotes from just a few of the many letters I received from MPs:

◆ *'I was concerned by what you say and have made appropriate representations to the Home Secretary.'* – Dr John Marek MP

◆ *'I am fully supportive...in total solidarity.'* – G.E.Bermingham MP

◆ *'I have already been in touch with the Government...I will certainly follow up the important issues you have raised with the Home Secretary. As you rightly say it is an important issue.'* – Sir Teddy Taylor MP

◆ *'I quite agree that human beings should treat all animals with respect and that vivisectors who break the law should be punished for their cruelty.'* – Dr Rudi Vis MP

◆ *'I have written to the Home Secretary...I fully agree that animals deserve to be treated with respect and vivisectors should obey the law.'* – Bill Olner MP

56

◆ 'I agree with your sentiments that animals have the right to be treated with respect and I will contact the Home Secretary regarding this matter.' – Stephen A. Godman MP

◆ '...vivisectors must obey the law in all their dealings with animals.' Dr Norman A. Godman MP

◆ 'I wish you every success with your campaign...and hope that it will result in more stringent checks on these facilities.' – Bob Russell MP

◆ '(You)...'are right to pursue this issue with the Home Secretary...By allowing the vivisector to infringe Acts of Parliament...the Home Secretary encourages others to ignore the plight of animals used for experimentation in medical programmes. This is wrong.' – Michael Fabricant MP

◆ 'I have written to Jack Straw...asking him for a full explanation. As the dominant species on this planet we have a duty to avoid any unnecessary suffering to other species...Many animal species, including mice, have nervous systems similar to those that we have and feel pain as we do. To disregard the effects of suffering in other creatures is to demean us as a human species and can lead to a coarsening of our sensitivities in treating humans and animals.' – Paul Flynn MP

◆ 'The very thought of animals being mistreated upsets me and, consequently, I actively support all the animal charities. Anybody who inflicts cruelty on animals, regardless of whether it is in the name of science, deserves no sympathy whatsoever and should feel the full force of the law.' – Gerry Steinberg MP

◆ 'I was concerned by the case you highlighted. If the facts are as you outlined in your letter (they were – VC), then clearly justice needs to be done. On this basis, I believe that anyone who breaks the law should be tried. As a result of your letter I have written to the Home Secretary to seek an explanation of his actions.' – Edward Davey MP

◆ 'I was horrified...and believe strongly that those responsible should be brought to justice. I would wholeheartedly condemn any failure to treat animals as humanely and painlessly as possible.' – Jonathan Shaw MP

Harry Cohen MP sent me a copy of the letter he had sent to Jack Straw. Here it is:

'Dear Minister

I enclose a self-explanatory letter I have received from Dr Vernon Coleman...

I am concerned at the contents.

If you do not know the identity of this cruel vivisector who apparently broke the law in regard to the mouse he was experimenting upon, then you should surely disclose it to the Police for possible prosecution.'

Please explain why you apparently have not done so.

From this example, are the public now to choose which crimes/criminals and evidence they report to the police, and which not?'

Other MPs wrote to me in similarly strong terms.

- *'You have my fullest support in what you are trying to do. I have been a long time opponent of vivisection and the way in which animals are mistreated, and the way in which many of the experiments are simply duplications…I believe that many of the experiments and examinations are no longer warranted. In my opinion the overwhelming majority of the British people would not consider them to be carried out in their interest. I would support any campaign that you mount which supports this view.'* – Councillor Mike Hancock CBE MP

- *'…the principle you represent has to be the right one…I think we agree on this subject.'* – Andrew George MP

- *'I believe vivisection is inhumane and should not be allowed to continue.'* – Elfyn Llwyd MP

Paul Tyler CBE, MP, a Liberal Democrat MP, wrote to tell me that his party wanted to strengthen the Protection of Animals Act 1911 and review the Animals (Scientific Procedures) Act 1986. And many other MPs have already written to me expressing their concern.

But Straw wouldn't budge. Uncharacteristically for a politician he remained resolute. He and the Government remained determined to protect the vivisector from prosecution.

Why?

I believe the answer is simple: the Government doesn't want the general public to know the sort of thing that goes on in laboratories.

The Government is committed to defending vivisection because the drug companies find it convenient. And the drug companies have made it clear that if vivisection is stopped in Britain then there will be an exodus of international drug companies. If and when the drug companies leave, a good many jobs (and substantial tax revenues) will go too.

99

'It's only a mouse,' vivisectors say, when excusing examples of cruelty to mice. They are, once again, showing their ignorance, their brutality and their heartlessness. Mice (and rats) suffer just as much as any other creatures. When tortured in laboratories they moan, cry and whimper just as much as any other creature.

Next time you see a mouse in your house watch carefully. You will see that mice show just as much fear as any other creature.

As I have already pointed out, vivisectors say that animals do not 'cry out'. They claim that animals merely vocalise and that the sounds they make are reflex sounds which mean nothing.

This is unthinking, ignorant nonsense, used as a convenient excuse for cruelty. There is no more evidence for this convenient claim than there was for the equally convenient claim, once widely believed, that black people do not suffer pain and are not sentient creatures.

100

Just a couple of decades ago doctors did not bother giving anaesthetics to human infants undergoing surgery on the grounds (completely unsubstantiated and based solely on myth) that babies do not suffer from pain. Doctors believed that human infants had immature nervous systems and, therefore, could not suffer pain and so although they used paralytic agents to stop the babies moving around while under the knife they used no anaesthetic. It was only when studies showed that babies who receive no pain medication take longer to recover from surgery that anaesthetists started giving babies an anaesthetic.

All this, may I remind you, was happening over a generation ago in hospitals in Europe and America and was authorised by doctors who must surely have seen their own infants crying during teething or because of the colic. The stupidity and barbarism of scientists is sometimes quite mind boggling.

Cruelty is cruelty.

101

Animals cannot tell us in our language that they do not suffer pain. But to say that because nice cannot describe their pain in our language they cannot suffer pain is as cruel and as irrational as it would be for English doctors to say that a German cannot be in pain because he cannot describe his pain in the English language.

Fish thrashing around on a hook are claimed to be acting under the control of some bizarre reflex action. Lobsters are supposed to be in no distress when they are boiled alive. Lambs and puppies are alleged to feel nothing when their tails are being docked.

Who says?

There is no evidence to support these claims. But there is plenty of evidence to support the notion that all creatures are capable of experiencing fear and can suffer pain.

102

In my book *Animal Rights Human Wrongs* I explained how our modern attitude to animals bears a great resemblance to the attitude whites once had towards black slaves. The whites assumed that blacks did not suffer and could not feel pain because it was convenient to them to adopt this belief. The belief allowed the whites to abuse and exploit the blacks without feeling bad about it. Animal abusers now use exactly the same excuses.

103

We can learn so much from animals.

Why, oh why, do our scientists insist on cutting up animals, ripping out their organs, injecting them with noxious chemicals and subjecting them to endless tortures when they could learn far, far more simply by observing them?

If architecture students wandered around the world knocking down cathedrals, palaces and other structural works of art, and then excused themselves by saying that they wanted to know more about how these buildings were constructed, we would describe them as wicked philistines. If a man in a white coat said that he was knocking down the Notre Dame in Paris because he thought it would help him design a suspension bridge or repair a mediaeval thatched cottage we would think him completely mad.

We can learn much from watching how animals behave and yet we always pretend that they are stupid. Anyone who talks about animals having thoughts is dismissed as 'romanticising' and accused of being anthropomorphic.

104

Many researchers who perform and support animal experiments also support experiments on human beings (they are particularly likely to experiment on the infirm and vulnerable) and sometimes argue that such experiments are justified either because they add to the sum of human knowledge or because they help doctors develop new types of treatment.

Here are just a few of the experiments conducted by vivisectors using human subjects:

◆ A woman scientist used a total of forty two babies aged between eleven days and two and a half years in experiments which involved holding the babies under water to see how they responded. The scientist reported that the babies clutched at the experimenters' hands and tried to wipe the water away from their faces. She seemed amazed that the 'ingestion of fluid was considerable' and made the infants cough.

♦ Drops were put into the eyes of women in order to study the formation of experimental cataracts.

♦ Children were given drugs to stop them making a natural recovery from a liver infection.

♦ Scientists deliberately injected patients with cancer cells to see whether or not they developed cancer.

Those who are opposed to the use of animals in experiments are invariably also opposed to the use of patients in experiments such as these.

Vivisectors, who perform experiments both on human beings and animals, are unlikely to criticise experiments of any kind.

105

Animal experiments delayed the practical availability of blood transfusions.

The first attempts used blood taken from animals. The patients all died. It wasn't until after 200 years of such experiments that a biologist called Landsteiner concentrated on human blood, discovered blood types and made blood transfusion a practical possibility.

106

Fraud is commonplace among animal researchers. One researcher who claimed that he had transplanted skin from black mice to white mice couldn't get the results he wanted so he simply inked in the transplant sites with a black felt-tipped pen. Another researcher killed dozens of rats to cover up an experiment which inconveniently contradicted the results of a previous experiment.

One major survey showed that almost 75% of all the work published contains invalid conclusions. An eminent American scientist testified before the USA Congress that he believed that 25% of scientific papers are now based at least in part on data that have been *intentionally* fudged. Inevitably, of course, many other scientists then quote those fudged papers – making their own work valueless.

107

There are many effective and safe ways available to test drugs. Human cell or organ cultures have been prepared from heart, kidney, liver, nerves, skin or any other part of the body. Drugs and other chemicals can be tested on these with remarkable speed and accuracy. For example, the World Health Organisation gave its approval for the use of cell cultures to replace mice during the production of yellow fever vaccine back in 1976. Cell cultures are much more accurate to use than animals and they produce much more accurate results. But do drug companies want accurate results? Many of their drugs are mass marketed for human beings after being 'passed' as safe as a result of animal tests. Effective testing would, I believe, result in many drugs never being given licences.

108

Most of the drugs put on the market these days are not new at all: they are made up of parts taken from existing drugs. By feeding existing knowledge into computers it is possible to make precise, speedy and cheap predictions about the likely consequences of giving drugs to patients. Scientists have also designed a computer program which replicates the complex physiological systems of the human body. These tests are much more effective than animal experiments.

109

One of the classic arguments used by animal abusers is to warn anyone thinking of joining or supporting the animal rights movement in general, and the anti-vivisection campaign in particular, is that if they oppose animal experiments (and are successful in calling for an end to animal experiments) they will, inevitably, be exposing themselves and their families to the risk that when they fall ill they will be deprived of life-saving treatments which would have been available had scientists been allowed to continue performing animal experiments.

'Of course we all love animals,' the hypocritical animal abusers will claim. 'We all wish that animal experiments weren't necessary. But the sad fact is that animal experiments are essential if we are to find a cure for (and here the animal abuser will insert a popular or fashionable disease or the name of the disease of which he knows the listener is frightened or the name of the disease which he knows already affects the listener or a member of his family) then animal experiments simply must continue.'

110

Pro-vivisectionists sometimes tell anti-vivisection campaigners that if they are going to be true to their beliefs, and not take advantage of the experiments on animals which have been done, then they (and their families) have to refuse to accept any modern medical treatment.

This ruthless trick, which is cruel and brutal as well as thoroughly dishonest, frightens many and puts many more off the idea of opposing animal experimentation. There is, in addition, the very real danger that many anti-vivisectionists will die prematurely because they have been encouraged, quite falsely, to believe that all modern medical treatments have been developed as a result of animal experimentation.

The simple truth, of course, is that since animal experiments are utterly irrelevant, and of no value whatsoever, there is no reason at all for anti-vivisectionists to refuse to accept modern treatments.

111

Rabbits are popular with vivisectors because their large eyes make a convenient test site for chemicals.

112

Experimenters avoid prosecution by keeping their laboratories locked, and by claiming that everything they do is part of an experiment (even the most unbelievable cruelty can be sanctioned legally if the researcher claims that the suffering was part of the experiment). If all else fails the vivisector will simply claim that he was trying to find a cure for cancer.

113

A survey of official reports from the Department of Agriculture in the USA showed that animals are being abused or neglected in more than four out of every five research institutions in America. Things are worse in Britain where secrecy is greater and opposition to animal experimentation is now (absurdly) regarded as terrorism.

This technique, which I have described as 'intellectual terrorism', works well for the animal abusers. It frightens ordinary people who may not have access to the facts and it undoubtedly frightens many who are simply so afraid of disease and death that they will cling to any hope which is offered.

114

The notion that those who oppose the use of animals in experiments should be officially classified as terrorists originated in Britain. This absurd nonsense was originally devised by the security services after the end of the Cold War with Russia was followed by the British Government making a deal with terrorists in Ireland. The security services found themselves with no threat against which to defend us and, therefore, with no reason for their existence.

Even though no one has ever been seriously injured or killed by an animal rights activist, pro-animal campaigners were selected as the most obvious alternative terrorists. Defending animals duly became the new terrorism. As a result of this almost every aspect of campaigning for and on behalf of animals is now illegal. At the same time, the democratic avenues have been closed as all major political parties take a hard line against animal rights and accept the commercially convenient view that animal experiments are essential. (Those who doubt the truth that democracy has disappeared should know that when local people and medical experts convinced a public enquiry that a new vivisection centre was not needed and should not go ahead the Government intervened, overruled the democratic process and authorised the new vivisection centre.) And now that the media has also followed suit (the international pharmaceutical industry is far too big a target for television or newspapers to dare take on) there is no opportunity for discussion of the issues either. It is hardly surprising that some who care about animals have become angry and frustrated.

115

The standard test used on rats to see if chemicals cause cancer gives results which can be applied accurately to human beings just 38% of the time. Put another way, this means that 62% of the time the experiments are wrong and misleading. Tossing a coin would give a 50% chance of obtaining useful information.

116

Researchers have created a 'test bed' made of human muscle tissue cells which can be used reliably to test anti-cancer drugs. What would you prefer to take: a drug tested on rats or one tested on cells exactly similar to the ones in your own body?

117

Animal researchers working for the Government have deliberately shot many animals to see what the wounds are like. Surgeons working with human casualties have stated firmly that these experiments have been of no value to them.

118

Digitalis, one of the best established and most effective drugs for the treatment of heart disease, is so toxic to animals that if we had relied on animal tests it would have never been cleared for use by humans.

119

Supporters of vivisection frequently claim that animal experiments enabled surgeons to perform transplant operations. This is untrue. Transplant operations have been performed on a wide range of animals (hearts, kidneys and even heads have been transplanted) but these experiments have consistently misled surgeons. Over a nine year period approximately four hundred heart transplant operations were carried out on dogs but the first human transplant operations died because of complications which had not arisen in animal experiments. Fundamental and crucial differences in anatomy and physiology mean that results from animal experiments are of no value. The first human patients are the real guinea pigs. The experiments on animals are of no practical value. The real problems occur after surgery has been performed and involve organ rejection and injection – problems which animal experiments do not help doctors overcome. Differences in anatomy and physiology mean that the results obtained from animal experiments cannot be used to help surgeons operating on people.

120

After I had defeated vivisectors in a series of public debates (some of them televised) the vivisectors simply decided to refuse to debate with me at all. For many years now television and radio producers who have tried to set up debates between vivisectors and myself have been told that if the debate is to go ahead then some other opponent must be found.

And the power of the drug industry (and the politicians and the parts of the medical establishment now owned by the drug industry) is so great that national newspapers are no longer willing to publish anything which questions the validity of animal experiments.

To my astonishment, national newspapers have even refused to carry advertisements on the subject of vivisection which I tried to put in.

For example, when I tried to put an advertisement inviting readers to visit my website to study evidence about vivisection into *The Guardian* the newspaper refused to run it. The newspaper claimed that they would not carry the advert for 'legal reasons' though no one would say precisely what it was about the advertisement which they thought might be against the law.

121

When Alexander Fleming discovered penicillin growing on a culture dish in 1928 he tested the drug on rabbits and discarded it when it seemed useless. Penicillin sat on a shelf, unused, for a decade after its discovery because of its ineffectiveness when given to infected rabbits. Later the drug was tested on a cat and a human patient at the same time. The cat died and the human being lived. If doctors had relied upon animal experiments to decide whether or not penicillin was of any value the drug would have been discarded long ago. Subsequent tests showed that if it had been tested on guinea pigs or hamsters, penicillin would have been abandoned as too toxic to use.

122

Pro-vivisection campaigners claim that without animal experiments there would have never been a vaccine against poliomyelitis. They are wrong.

The number of deaths from polio had fallen dramatically some time before the first polio vaccine was introduced. Better food, better housing, cleaner water and better sanitation had all led to a fall. In fact the evidence shows that the introduction of the vaccine led to more patients with polio rather than fewer. In Tennessee, USA, the number of poliomyelitis victims the year before vaccination became compulsory was 119, but the year after vaccination was introduced the number rose to 386. In North Carolina, the number of cases before vaccination was 78 while the number after the vaccine became compulsory rose to 313. There are similar figures for other American states.

The first breakthrough in the development of a poliomyelitis vaccine was made in 1949 with the aid of a human tissue culture. But when the first practical vaccine was prepared in the 1950's, monkey kidney tissue was used because that was standard laboratory practice. Researchers didn't realise that one of the viruses commonly found in monkey kidney cells can cause cancer in humans. If human cells had been used to prepare the vaccine (as they could and should have been and as they are now) the original poliomyelitis vaccine would have been much safer.

In 1982, the World Health Organization recommended that tests on animals are unnecessary when human cells are used to produce the poliomyelitis vaccine. Over 250,000 rabbits, guinea pigs and mice were killed unnecessarily.

123

If researchers had tested aspirin on animals it would have never been authorised. Aspirin can be toxic to rats, mice, dogs, cats, monkeys and guinea pigs though it is effective and safe for people.

Arsenic is dangerous to humans but doesn't have anything like the same effect when given to rats, mice or sheep.

Steroids damage mice in a way that they do not affect people. Morphine sedates human beings but excites cats, goats and horses while insulin produces deformities in chickens, mice and rabbits.

124

Coleman's First Law of Medicine is that if a patient has two diseases it is a fair bet that the second disease will have been caused by the treatment for the first. Without the drug industry's reliance on animal testing the incidence of drug-induced disease would be much lower.

125

Animal abusers sometimes assume that it is only humans who can communicate with one another. And yet even such tiny creatures as bees can communicate with one another very effectively. A bee can, for example, tell other bees the direction, distance and value of pollen sources. Animal abusers generally dismiss animal noises as simply that (noises) but people who have taken the time and trouble to listen carefully to the extraordinary variety of noises made by whales have found that there are patterns of what can only be described as speech. Whales talk to one another.

It is generally assumed that parrots merely repeat words they have heard without understanding what they mean. This is not true. When a psychologist left her parrot at the vet's surgery for an operation the parrot, whose name was Alex, called out: 'Come here. I love you. I'm sorry. I want to go back.' The parrot clearly thought that he was being punished for some crime he had committed.

Another parrot, in New Jersey, USA saved the life of its owner by calling for help. 'Murder! Help! Come quick!' cried the parrot. When neighbours ran to the scene of the crime they found the parrot's owner lying on the floor, unconscious, bleeding from a gash in his neck. The doctor who treated the man said that without the parrot's cries he would have died. The same parrot woke his owner and neighbours when a fire started in the house next door.

How arrogant the animal abusers are to assume that human beings are the only species capable of communicating with one another, and of formulating a formal system of language. Vivisectors frequently laugh at the animals they torture and abuse. It is no coincidence that the German concentration camp guards in the Second World War laughed and mocked their victims.

Vivisectors talk about 'sending a mouse to college' when they want to raise funds for experiments.

Human beings who have taken the time to do so have found that they have been able to communicate well with chimpanzees and numerous other animals. It is known too that monkeys can grasp the concept of numbers and can learn to count.

And yet I have on my desk a photograph of a monkey taken from a vivisection laboratory. The monkey has the word 'CRAP' written (or carved) on his or her forehead.

Primates will often strive to make the peace after a hostile encounter. Other uninvolved primates may help begin and cement the reconciliation. And yet vivisectors are given legal licences allowing them to do horrific things to these animals.

We have the power to do what we will with creatures of other species. But no one has given us the right.

126

The drug industry spends a good deal of money on setting up organisations around the world to lobby for vivisection. Drug companies even help sponsor small groups of campaigners who protest noisily (and with massive media support) on behalf of animal experiments. Naturally, those who oppose the use of animals in experiments must raise their funding themselves.

127

Doctors wouldn't test a drug intended for old people on children (or the other way round). So why do drug companies test drugs intended for pregnant women on rats? No one would test a drug for pre-menstrual problems on small boys and yet that would make far more sense than testing such a drug on male rats.

128

An American woman suffered eye damage when she used a shampoo. She tried to claim damages from the company concerned on the basis that the drug had also proved to be an irritant when tested on animals. However, the court in Ohio, USA, where the case was heard, ruled in favour of the company on the grounds that there was no evidence to show that tests done on rabbits could be used to predict what would be likely to happen in humans. So, why did the company test on rabbits? Were they planning to sell their shampoo to rabbits?

129

A doctor told the drug company E.R.Squibb and Sons that a drug that they had prepared for the treatment of diarrhoea damaged the eyesight of rabbits. Squibb's own scientists then subsequently found that the drug blinded and killed two calves. They later also found that the drug blinded and killed grown cattle and that it killed or paralysed dogs. Nevertheless, Squibb launched the drug on the market and obtained approval to sell it for use in humans.

When Squibb was taken to court by a woman who lost her sight and became paralysed after taking the drug, the drug company denied negligence saying that they knew of no evidence that the drug had adverse effects on human beings. They apparently dismissed the animal research as irrelevant on the grounds that animals are different to humans.

130

All animal research is an affront to human dignity – let alone an insult to the animals involved.

131

Cigarette companies spent millions on research. And yet whenever the results got close to suggesting a link between cigarette smoking and disease the cigarette companies came up with some bizarre explanations for their results. For example, here is a slightly surreal exchange which took place between a lawyer representing the family of a woman who had died of lung cancer after smoking cigarettes for 43 years, and the president of the tobacco company involved. The lawyer asked the tobacco company president to explain the purpose of an experiment in which the shaven backs of mice were painted with tars derived from cigarette smoke.

President: 'To try to reduce tumours on the backs of mice.'

Lawyer: 'It had nothing to do with the health and welfare of human beings?'

President: 'That's correct.'

Lawyer: 'How much did the study cost?'

President: 'Probably more than $15 million.'

132

Who pays for animal experiments? You do. Vivisection is big business, largely funded by taxpayers, shareholders, patients and people who put money into charity collecting tins in the mistaken belief that their donations will help fight diseases such as cancer or heart disease. You pay for the animals, you pay for the equipment used in the laboratories and you pay the salaries of the vivisectors who perform the experiments. Finally, you pay with your health because animal experiments are the excuse for licensing and marketing drugs which are not safe for human use.

133

Animals which are used in scientific procedures only appear once in the official figures – however many times they are tortured. So if a baboon is used in twelve experiments the statistics will show just one use of an animal. Long-term experiments disappear from the statistics after the first year. All this helps keep the official number of experiments down much lower than it is.

134

The use of primates in medical research is increasing. Recent statistics for the European Union showed a 14% increase (to 10,362) in the number of primates used by vivisectors.

135

Animals used in laboratories suffer mental and physical distress; some species suffer from problems such as ulcers and heart abnormalities as a result of their incarceration. The use of experimental subjects who suffer so much from stress destroys any slight validity an experiment might have and utterly invalidates the results of such research.

136

Apart from the obvious anatomical differences there are many subtle physiological differences between the sort of animals who are used in experimental procedures and the human body. In addition many of the diseases which kill or cripple human beings do not affect any other members of the animal kingdom. So, for example, cancers which affect human beings are quite different from the cancers which affect mice. Arthritis, multiple sclerosis and high blood pressure all commonly affect human beings but don't usually affect animals. The type of tuberculosis which affects people is very different to the type that is produced artificially in animals.

137

Animal experiments are often poorly planned and sloppily executed; it is clear that those performing animal experiments have little understanding of the way that research should be planned or conducted in order to obtain worthwhile results. Researchers investigating the quality of animal experiments for the *British Medical Journal* concluded that: 'Many animal studies were of poor methodological quality.'

138

Food dyes and other chemicals are tested on animals either by force-feeding the animals huge quantities of the food concerned (the equivalence of several tons a day for two years is not unusual) or by injecting the substance directly into the animal's organs. The food dyes are given to animals which would never eat the foods in which they are used. Just what the purpose is of these absurd tests has never been explained.

139

Vivisectors around the world 'use' around 250 million animals a year. That's 100,000 to 125,000 animals killed every hour. Or around 1,000 animals every thirty seconds.

140

A few years ago I was invited to speak about animal issues at the university in Johannesburg, South Africa. There was initially some difficulty in finding a supporter of animal abuse in general (and vivisection in particular) who was prepared to debate the issue with me in public. The only local academic who was prepared to defend his work in public agreed to do so on condition that the entire debate was conducted in Afrikaans. As he undoubtedly well knew, I do not speak Afrikaans.

Eventually, a speaker was flown in from Cape Town to support the contention that scientists should be allowed to continue performing animal experiments.

One of the main tenets of her argument was that since animals do not have souls they do not have rights. This is, of course, a point of view first put forward by René Descartes a long time ago. Descartes believed (with no evidence whatsoever to support the belief) that non-human animals lack souls, intelligence and the ability to feel pleasure, pain or, indeed, anything. According to Descartes if you hit an animal then it would cry out for just the same reason that a clock chimes or a bell rings.

I recall rather angrily asking the woman in South Africa how she knew that animals do not have souls. 'Has your god told you this?' I asked. I seem to remember a lack of a clear response to this question.

141

When the lives of six healthy young men were endangered during a clinical trial which went wrong scientists claimed that the unexpectedly severe reactions suffered by the men surprised them. The drug had previously been tested on rabbits and at least one monkey and the animal tests had produced what were later described as falsely reassuring results. The men suffered massive inflammation and terrible pains. Three were critically ill.

Why?

One explanation given was that the dramatic response in humans was a result of protein differences between people and other species.

But why was anyone surprised?

All animals are different.

142

Time and time again, drugs which produce miraculous cures when given to mice fail miserably when given to people.

143

When sweeteners or other food products are shown to cause cancer or other serious problems when given to animals (as happens with some frequency) the inconvenient results are dismissed on the grounds that animals are different to people.

144

The USA General Accounting Office has reported that 52% of new drugs cause serious adverse effects in humans that had not been predicted by animal experiments.

145

The drug Vioxx seemed safe when tested on animals. Nine out of eleven studies on mice or rats showed that it had no adverse effects on animal hearts or blood vessels. Six different animal studies in four different species showed Vioxx protected against heart attacks and vascular disease. As a result of the animal tests, one researcher claimed that Vioxx should be considered as a treatment for human heart disease. The drug was widely prescribed as an anti-inflammatory medicine, suitable for arthritis sufferers.

But according to America's Food and Drug Administration Vioxx may have contributed to 27,785 heart attacks and sudden cardiac deaths between 1999 and 2003. It has been estimated that Vioxx might have contributed to the development of heart and vascular disease in around 140,000 Americans.

Not many people die from arthritis.

There's another twist to this story.

In the year 2000, just about a year after the launch of Vioxx, a study of more than 8,000 human patients suggested that those taking the drug faced a significantly increased risk of having a heart attack.

But subsequent animal experiments continued to suggest that such drugs could reduce the risk of heart disease, rather than increase it.

And the authorities preferred to take notice of the animal tests rather than the experiences doctors had reported with real human patients.

146

Manufacturers are supposed to show that their drugs are safe and, to a certain extent, effective. They do not have to show that their drugs are necessary.

147

In the Multicenter Evaluation of In Vitro Cytotoxicity it was shown that tests done on human cells in laboratories are far more accurate than tests on animals in deciding whether or not chemicals are toxic.

The Multicenter Evaluation of In Vitro Cytotoxicity program showed that rat and mouse tests were only 65% accurate in predicting lethal blood concentrations of chemicals in humans. But a combination of computer modelling and human-cell tests predicted chemical toxicity with 80% precision.

Despite this, civil servants still demand animal tests. It's what they're used to. It's what they've always done.

And drug companies don't push them into changing because animal tests are commercially convenient.

The result is that patients and animals lose out.

148

According to a 1998 article in the *Journal of the American Medical Association*, more than 100,000 Americans are killed every year by adverse reactions to drugs.

149

More than 90% of drugs that appear safe in animal tests prove too dangerous for human use when initially tested on people.

150

More than half of all approved drugs have to be withdrawn or re-labelled because they cause serious or lethal effects when finally given licences for human use. And yet animal tests are relied on heavily in pre-marketing tests.

151

'Leading journal *Nature Reviews Drug Discovery* published a review of the evidence that animals are reliable predictors of toxic effects in humans. The authors found that the evidence was 'fragmentary', with the few published studies pointing to 'significant over-and under-prediction of adverse effects from animal studies that varies with the particular organ or system.'

'The review also highlighted the lack of basic data needed for a scientific assessment of animal testing, such as measures of predictive power and their statistical significance.'

'As it stands, the evidence suggests animal tests may be unduly sensitive, wrongly predicting toxicity in compounds that are in fact harmless to humans. If so it would be an ironic twist to the widely held belief that tests on animals are crucial to the advancement of medicine, as they may in fact be blocking the development of many safe and effective new treatments.'

'Yet in the absence of large-scale studies comparing drug responses in animals and humans, it is impossible to know.'
Financial Times,

152

Vivisectors claim that the animals they torture and kill are well looked after before and during experiments.

This is a lie.

Animals are often kept in tiny cages for years – alone, terrified and able to hear the screams and cries of those creatures ahead of them on the death list.

I've unearthed the official figures for the amount of floor space animals are allowed in laboratories – and the length of time they could spend in those cages.

You might like to measure out the size of these cages on your living room carpet. And then imagine the horror of your family pet living in a cage like that for years – without love or companionship, in constant fear and probably in severe pain too.

1. Dog
Possible life expectancy: 35 years
Size of cage: 8 square feet

2. Cat
Possible life expectancy: 20 years
Size of cage: 3 square feet

3. Rabbit
Possible life expectancy: 15 years
Size of cage: 3 square feet

4. Monkey
Possible life expectancy: 30 years
Size of cage: 6 square feet

5. Rat
Possible life expectancy: 4 years
Size of cage: 0.4 square feet

6. Mouse
Possible life expectancy: 3 years
Size of cage: 0.4 square feet

7. Guinea pig
Possible life expectancy: 7 years
Size of cage: 0.7 square feet

8. Hamster
Possible life expectancy: 2 years
Size of cage: 0.34 square feet

153

It is difficult to avoid the sad but inevitable conclusion that animal experiments are used because they are financially expedient. Animals are not just relatively cheap to use but there are also clear commercial advantages for the world's most successful and ruthless industry: the drug industry. The bizarre but inescapable conclusion is that drug companies depend on the fact that animal experiments are unreliable in order to get their new products onto the market without testing them properly. The very unreliability and unpredictably of animal experiments makes them valuable. Drug companies test on animals so that they can say that they have tested their drugs before marketing them. If the tests show that the drugs do not cause serious disorders when given to animals the companies say: 'There you are! We have tested our drug – and have proved it to be safe!' If, on the other hand, tests show that a drug does cause serious problems when given to animals the companies say: 'The animal experiments are, of course, unreliable and cannot be used to predict what will happen when the drug is given to humans. We have, however, tested our drug.' This double-edged absurdity, which only works because of the enormous influence which the pharmaceutical industry holds over governments and regulatory authorities, and which would sound like a nightmare conjured up by a paranoid lunatic if it were not true, means that the industry never loses and patients never win.

154

Drug companies will sometimes perform animal experiments on products made by other companies. The only reason I can think of for a company to do animal experiments on another company's products is to obtain results which might add to the confusion and suggest that a product may not be safe. It is always possible to obtain disturbing results if you give a drug to enough different species of animals.

155

When the drug company Roussel, one of the biggest in Europe, was taken to court by the British Government because of advertisement claims for an anti-arthritis drug called Surgam the company, which had claimed in advertisements published in the *British Medical Journal* that the drug was gentle on the stomach was asked to produce the evidence for this claim. The only evidence Roussel produced was from experimental studies on two animal tissues (neither of which was stomach tissue) which they had combined in order to support their claim. Even the expert witnesses called by Roussel in its defence testified that data from animals could not be extrapolated safely to patients.

You might imagine that after this fiasco drug companies would be wary about making claims (either for efficacy or safety) based on animal experiments. You would be wrong. Nothing has changed. Medical journals still allow drug companies to publish advertisements for drugs which have been tested on animals. I know of no medical journal editor who has refused to accept advertisements for products which have been tested on animals.

156

Scientists continue performing animal experiments because they have now been used for so long and by so many scientists that thousands of reputations would be irrevocably shattered if it were accepted by the research industry that the work they have been doing for so many years was fatally flawed. It is remarkably quick and simple to plan, research and write and publish scientific papers if you are using animals. Decent and useful research, involving human patients, is much harder to organise – and since most of the medical scientists using animals in experiments are not medically qualified most of them would not, in any case, be allowed to perform any sort of clinical research. Prolific publishing (usually accompanied by optimistic conclusions about the value of the research) is the best way to ensure a steady income from grants. It is the quantity not the quality of research which governs the financial results. Charities which pay for much of the animal research done want to be able to fill their annual reports with impressive and optimistic accounts of research in progress.

The university scientists who perform animal experiments outside the pharmaceutical industry are undoubtedly grateful to the industry for creating and maintaining the myths which support the milieu in which they work. And the industry in turn, recognising that the fact that universities still perform animal experiments supports the validity of their work is also grateful: often commissioning highly-paid research work from 'independent' scientists in universities and colleges. In some universities whole departments are financed exclusively by the drug industry.

The myth that animal experiments are of value to doctors and patients is sustained because the vast majority of doctors – the only people who could expose the absurd rigmarole for the sham that it is – are either uninterested in how drugs are tested (and apathetic about the dishonesty involved) or are so beholden to the industry that they are unwilling or unable to criticise it.

157

The vast majority of the thousands of medical journals in existence rely to a greater or lesser extent on drug industry advertising to stay alive and so the editors of these journals are reluctant to publish anything critical of any aspect of the system as it operates.

Articles criticising the drug industry, the way drugs are tested or the use of animal experiments are even rarer than honest, public-spirited politicians. The existence of so many medical journals, largely sustained by drug company advertising, means that there is a steady and constant demand for new scientific papers. And so the whole system is self-supporting. The industry needs to publish research papers in order to satisfy the regulatory authorities and to convince possibly sceptical doctors that their products have been well-tested and proven to be both efficacious and safe. Independent researchers need to publish papers in order to provide the charities which fund their work with evidence with which to impress their subscribers and donors. And the journals need articles to publish.

158

Those who perform and defend animal experiments sometimes try to explain away the differences which exist between the results obtained when drugs are given to animals and when drugs are given to human beings by claiming that the dosages used when giving drugs to animals are too high. Strangely, they never bother to explain why they deliberately make the dosages they give so high as to be of no value. The truth is that no one does know how much of a drug to give to an animal in the hope of obtaining results which might be considered vaguely relevant to an animal (a human being) weighing a hundred or a thousand times as much and having entirely different physiological and anatomical systems.

159

The differences in results obtained when giving drugs to children and adults is so vast that paediatricians frequently complain when drug companies fail to perform special trials on children. Similarly, all good physicians know that adult human beings of different sizes and different ages may respond in different ways to the same drug. (There is something quite absurd about giving a 7 stone woman and a 20 stone man exactly the same dose of an antibiotic for example). And many drug companies now warn prescribers that special dosage rules must be followed when giving drugs to elderly patients.

It should, therefore, be clear to anyone with any knowledge of physiology that the only possible argument for trying out drugs on animals is in the hope that the tests will show signs of toxicity. However, even this hope is dashed because there is a huge amount of evidence available to show that animals frequently react quite differently to human beings when given drugs. A cat can't be expected to react the same way as a dog or a sheep or a cow or a mouse or a guinea pig or a rat or a human being when given a drug. Of course, the simple law of averages means that occasionally there will be results which seem of value – but how is anyone supposed to know which results to take notice of and which to ignore? Most doctors, even many who support vivisection, will confirm that animal experiments can be misleading. After the *European Medical Journal* published a survey showing that 88% of doctors agreed that animal experiments can be misleading because of anatomical and physiological differences between animals and humans the editor of the *British Medical Journal* wrote to me to say that he felt that most doctors would agree with the phrase that 'laboratory experiments performed on animals can be misleading because of anatomical and physiological differences between animals and humans'. One University Dean of Medicine wrote to me expressing his surprise that the survey did not find that 100% of the doctors who took part in the survey believed that animal experiments could be misleading.

The problem, of course, is that no doctor can tell you which animal experiments are going to be most misleading.

160

If you test a drug on eight species of animal and the drug turns out to cause cancer in two of those animals, to cause liver problems in another two, to cause blindness in two more and to be quite safe in a final pair should you accept the results from the two that develop cancer, the two who develop liver problems, the two who become blind or the two who remain well?

In practice, all the 'uncomfortable' or 'commercially inconvenient' results are ignored (as shown by the number of drugs currently freely available for doctors to prescribe which are known to cause serious problems in animals). The experiments which show no illness in animals are the ones which are considered relevant.

161

The absurdity of the whole business of giving drugs to animals, and expecting to obtain useful results, is taken even further away from logic and practicality by the knowledge that animals in cages behave quite differently to animals in the wild and the understanding that since diet, exercise patterns and genetics all have significant effects on the way human beings respond to disease and drug therapy it is possible that these, or other influences, may also affect animals in some way when they are given drugs.

162

Experiments have shown that vasectomy operations accelerated arteriosclerosis in monkeys but no one seems to have taken any notice of this discovery and several million vasectomy operations are still performed on human males each year.

163

Scientists and entrepreneurs have claimed that in the future it will be possible to save human lives by breeding and then implanting organs from animals which have been genetically altered so that they are not rejected by the human tissues.

The theory is that by implanting human genes in animals such as pigs the scientists will be able to breed creatures which will be part animal and part human being.

The scientists believe that when the hearts, livers and other organs are chopped out of these hybrid animals and stuck into human patients they won't be rejected.

I have several reasons for objecting to these experiments.

First, I have strong moral and ethical objections to the idea of mixing human and animal genes to create new animals.

I know that it is unfashionable to have moral or ethical objections to anything scientific these days but just where is this sort of research going to stop? I have no doubt that if scientists mixed postmen genes with whippet genes we could get our letters delivered more quickly but at what point does the creature the scientists are creating stop being an animal and start acquiring human rights? Can you legally tear the organs out of a creature which is part human? How many human genes do you need to get a credit card? If one of these new hybrid creatures starts getting mail from the *Readers' Digest* will the scientists still be able to tear its liver out without having their collars felt?

Second, who gave scientists permission to start messing around with animals in this way? Unbelievably, scientists are claiming patents on some of the animals they're creating.

Third, no one else seems to have thought about this (or dared to mention it) but where is the money going to come from to pay for all the extra transplant operations? We'll need regiments of extra surgeons and thousands of new hospitals.

At the moment it is the shortage of transplant organs which is saving nations from bankruptcy but when surgeons can pop into their nearest supermarket and pick out a hybrid heart 'Ready for Use: From the Freezer to the Chest Cavity' we're going to have big problems.

Fourth, when are things going to go seriously, horrifyingly, frighteningly, blood chillingly wrong? When men in white coats say that everything is foolproof and nothing can go wrong I get this funny tingling feeling down my spine. Things will go wrong. Believe me. Things will go wrong. Remember: one in six patients in hospital is already there because doctors and medical scientists have screwed up.

Fifth, what about the enormous religious and cultural problems this is all going to create? If you try flying into the Middle East with a pigskin belt holding your trousers up you're likely to be deported and have your belt confiscated. What happens if you've got a pig's heart pumping away in your chest? ('I'm sorry, sir, we'll have to confiscate the heart but you'll be free to leave the country afterwards.')

It makes me go cold inside. Are we all really this desperate to live forever?

164

The establishment is wary of the anti-vivisection argument because it has been encouraged to believe that those who favour it are simply cranks – fired by an over-zealous enthusiasm for the welfare of animals and a failure to understand the requirements of science.

The image of the anti-vivisection movement has been deliberately clouded by lies, deceit and propaganda.

165

It is no more possible to support animal experimentation in logical argument than it would be to support slavery or to oppose the emancipation of women. If vivisection were stopped tomorrow it would never be introduced again because no one would ever be able to find an argument supporting its introduction.

Animal experiments are so barbaric and so indefensible on moral, ethical, scientific or medical grounds that once they are stopped no one will ever dream of letting them start again.

However, the battle against vivisection (which should be fought by those who care for the safety of human patients as well as animals) must be fought not just against waves of prejudice but also against apparently endless seas of ignorance and indifference. Confused and frightened by the pro-vivisection campaigns (which I regard as the crudest and most vicious form of intellectual terrorism ever seen – usually being dependent on the 'if we stop animal experiments then children will die' argument) ordinary members of the public do nothing. The experiments are done in their name but they remain silent.

166

Some politicians who support the anti-vivisection campaign insist that we should aim for a pan European ban on the grounds that a single country ban would be impractical.

It would only be impractical for the drug industry.

Can you imagine the chaos that would exist if the industry had to produce drugs that had not been tested on animals just for one country? A single country ban would quite quickly lead to a universal ban.

If, for example, Britain or Germany announced that it was no longer going to allow the sale of drugs which had been tested on animals then animal testing would stop very quickly. The drug companies wouldn't move their testing procedures to Russia or Africa (as the politicians now claim they will) because there wouldn't be any point in doing any animal experiments at all.

167

Animal experiments will never be stopped by waiting for the legislators to take action because the drug companies control the legislators. Animal experiments will be stopped by public opinion forcing politicians to take action (in just the same way that public opinion has led the way to all other great social changes). Modern politicians do not lead – they simply (eventually) follow public opinion.

168

Iatrogenesis (doctor-induced disease) is one of the commonest causes of serious ill health in the western world. It is usually put in the top three causes of death – alongside cancer and circulatory disease.

If the money spent on animal testing were spent on proper clinical trials (not to mention preventive medicine programmes) then far more lives would be saved.

169

It is important to remember that the pharmaceutical industry, which is marketing led rather than being led by patients' requirements, has no interest in patient welfare.

170

Animal experimentation is done with a false mantle of science by men and women who claim to be educated and civilised. It is based on lies and ruthlessly used to make money. A side effect is that millions of patients are made ill. Those who perform, support and defend animal experimentation have betrayed us all.

171

It is widely assumed among journalists that the scientific establishment is, and always has been, wholly in favour of animal experiments.

This simply isn't so, as the following quotes, taken from scientific journals prove:

◆ 'The discipline (clinical pharmacology) first evolved from the recognition that studies in rats do not give doctors enough information about the way drugs really behave in the human body.' – *Hospital Doctor*

◆ 'Doctors wanting to defend Britain's 3.2 million scientific procedures on living animals will want to know much more about what they are defending than this book (*Statistics of Scientific Procedures on Living Animals*) tells them. It's impossible to answer such simple questions as how many procedures are accounted for by the search for new drugs and to which pharmacological groups they belong. (Doctors may find it difficult to muster much enthusiasm for the nth beta-blocker or the n+1th non-steroidal anti-inflammatory drug.) We're not told how many purely psychological studies were performed, although there is the tantalising detail that for 11,100 procedures the induction of psychological stress was integral to the procedure. (Why? What was learnt, or hoped to be learnt, from frightening rodents, reptiles, amphibians, and fish?)' – *The British Medical Journal*

- 'Despite the fact that nearly all analgesics are tested on animals prior to their use in man very little is known about the effects of clinical doses of analgesics on physiology and behaviour in normal rodents.' – *Laboratory Animals*

- 'Since the results of these animal studies were inconsistent, it seemed that the only way to discover more about the cellular events in new bone was to study the process in man.' – *The Lancet*

- 'Experimental models are far removed from clinical reality...,' – *Scientific American*

- 'Despite the claims of the animal modellers, their studies have largely been irrelevant to psychiatric problems or have lent token support to human studies...The enormous field of mother-infant separation and deprivation research in animals does not contain a single study that had a discernible clinical impact...The research did reveal marked variation within and between species that casts considerable doubt on extrapolations to humans, and that vitiates any results that seemingly 'confirm' human studies.' – *The Veterinary Record*

- 'The predictive value for man of toxicological testing in animals is open to question.' – *Prescribers Journal*

- '...we currently are unable to assess clinical pain objectively and reliably in animals.' – *Laboratory Animals*

172

Those who abuse animals frequently claim that animals do not need or deserve special treatment because they are not 'sentient' creatures – in other words that they are not conscious creatures with the capacity to suffer and/or experience enjoyment or happiness.

A similar argument was used by those who supported slavery. The slavery proponents argued that Negroes did not blush because they were incapable of shame and were, therefore, not fully human.

Interestingly a number of animals and birds have been observed to blush when excited (and do, therefore, satisfy these traditional requirements for 'human' behaviour). The Tasmanian devil, the turkey, macaws and monkeys are among the other creatures known to blush. (Macaws, for example, have been reported to blush when accidentally falling while clambering down off a perch.)

It was also argued that black people were not capable of looking after themselves or their own interests because they were irrational. This was regarded as a good excuse for keeping black people in 'protective custody' and for exposing them to unlimited abuse.

173

Showing an extraordinary level of intellectual emptiness supporters of animal abuse have claimed, when defending fox hunting, that although animals are not sentient and have no feelings they 'enjoy' being hunted. It is difficult to see how anyone can possibly sustain the argument that animals who are not sentient can 'enjoy' anything.

The supporters of animal abuse are full of contradictions, double-speak and deceit. People who deny that animals can suffer will claim that animals can be cruel. How can an animal be cruel if the animal to which it is supposed to be cruel cannot suffer? How can an allegedly non-sentient animal be cruel?

174

As with humans, stress is a major factor in the development of disease in animals. But laboratory scientists who work with animals do not recognise the problem — or the effect it must have on the outcome of their experiments.

Scientists put captured healthy wild African green monkeys in separate cages in order to measure the effects of stress on their immune systems. The monkeys rapidly fell ill. Their immune systems deteriorated and even though the animals were given all the nutrients they needed they contracted infectious diseases. Some of the monkeys died.

Other studies have shown exactly the same thing. Animals which normally live in the wild do not adapt well when kept in cages. Their immune systems collapse when they are separated from their families and friends and shut up in laboratories. Their digestive systems malfunction.

Even if wild animals are caught when still young they will often die within weeks or months if they are locked in a cage. Creatures as varied as gorillas and white sharks all tend to fall ill and die if locked up.

An animal's immune system is inextricably linked to its surroundings and to its exposure to stress. All this means, of course, that when vivisectors lock animals up in cages in order to conduct experiments they are altering the outcome of their experiment before they even start.

Under normal circumstances an animal will use its own internal mechanical and physiological mechanisms to protect itself from illness. It will rest when it needs to rest. It will groom itself to keep itself clean. It will change its diet when appropriate. And when it is ill it will seek out plants or other substances with which to medicate itself.

By locking an animal in a cage the experimenters have altered the surroundings and, therefore, the animal's susceptibility, habits, instincts and capacity to heal itself. The animal's body will react differently according to how long he or she has been locked up and how much stress he or she is experiencing. To conduct any sorts of tests on animals in such an unpredictable state is clearly utterly pointless.

175

Lawyers who have studied the evidence for and against the use of animal experiments have been convinced by the argument that animal experiments are so unreliable as to be useless. Consider this quote from the *Idaho Law Review*:

'Animal studies have no place in the courtroom. They suffer from inherent and incurable defects that make them entirely unreliable as proof of human response to toxic substances. They fail to account for astonishing differences between animal species and humans; indeed they fail to account for large differences in test results that occur within individual animal species. They rest on unproven assumptions that humans and animals will respond similarly to the same substances and that large doses administered under experimental conditions can be reliably translated into lower doses more commonly encountered in the real world.'

176

Animals, like people, are capable of loving their partner, their families, their children, their leaders, their teachers, their friends and others who are important to them. An ape will show exactly the same signs of love and affection when dealing with her baby as a human mother will when dealing with her baby. Both will look longingly, tickle and play with the infant. Both feed their young, wash them, risk their lives for them and put up with their noise and unruly behaviour.

Anyone who doubts that animals love their young should stand outside a farmyard when a calf has been taken away from a cow and listen to the heart breaking cries of anguish which result. Who knows what inner pain accompanies those cries from a creature who does not normally vocalise in the same way that other animals do.

Even fish will risk their lives to protect their young. In his seminal work *The Universal Kinship* (first published in 1906 and now largely forgotten) J. Howard Moore described how he put his hand into a pond near the nest of a perch. The courageous fish guarding the nest chased Moore's hand away several times and when Moore's hand was not removed quickly enough would nip it vigorously several times.

Lewis Gompertz, who lived from 1779 to 1861 and was a potent champion of the rights of blacks, women and the poor (and, indeed, all oppressed human beings) was also a powerful champion of animals and was a founder of the Royal Society for the Prevention of Cruelty to Animals. (His credibility is, I feel, dramatically enhanced by the knowledge that quite early on he was forced out of the Society). In his book *Moral Inquiries On the Situation Of Man And Of Brutes* Gompertz wrote: 'From some birds we may learn real constancy in conjugal affection, though in most instances their contracts only last for one season, but how strict do they keep this. They have no laws, no parchments, no parsons, no fear to injuring their characters, not even their own words to break in being untrue to each other: but their virtue is their laws, their parchments, their parsons, and their reputation; their deeds are their acts, their acts – their deeds: and from their own breasts do they honestly tear down to line the beds of their legitimate offspring.'

Gompertz described an incident illustrating the wisdom of blackbirds. 'I observed a male blackbird flying about in an extreme state of agitation,' he wrote. 'And on my going to discover the cause of it, the bird retreated from me as I followed it, till it stopped at a nest containing a female bird sitting upon her eggs, near which there was a cat: in consequence of this I removed the cat, and the bird became quiet. After that, whenever the cat was about the place, the blackbird would come near my window, and would in the same manner direct me to some spot where the cat happened to be stationed.'

Gompertz also wrote about a male blackbird who had attacked a cat who had caught its female partner, and wrote about three true incidents which illustrated animal kindness and wisdom. The first concerned two goats which had met one another on a narrow path between two precipices. There was no room for the two goats to turn or pass and so one of the goats lay down, allowing the other to walk over it. The second incident involved a horse who had been hurt by a nail when he had been shod. Finding it painful to walk he had gone back to the farrier and shown him his hoof. The third incident involved a sheep dog who jumped into freezing cold water and successfully rescued another dog which had been floating on a lump of ice. 'I would now fain ask,' wrote Gompertz, 'if all this does not show reason and virtue?'

J. Howard Moore described how monkeys may adopt the orphans of deceased members of their tribe and how two crows fed a third crow which was wounded. The wound was several weeks old and the two crows had clearly been playing 'good Samaritans' for that time.

Darwin wrote about a blind pelican which was fed with fish which were brought to it by pelican friends who normally lived thirty miles away.

Other writers have reported that strong males in a herd of vicunas will lag behind to protect the weaker and slower members of their herd from possible predators.

177

Before slavery was abolished black people who fell in love were regarded as enjoying simple 'animal lust' as a result of 'animal attraction'.

When black people formed life-long pairs this was dismissed as nothing more than a response to an 'instinct'. The same thing is said about animals (with just as little evidence to support it).

Who gives humans the right to argue that animals do not show emotions?

Animal abusers sneer and say that animals who show love are merely acting according to instinct. But who says? Where is the evidence for this claim? Why do animal abusers have the right to make statements with no evidence whatsoever in support?

Why don't the animal abusers follow a consistent line and argue that human mothers who show love for their human babies are merely following their instincts?

(Of course, people change their views when it suits them. Even vivisectors and hunters, who claim that animals have no feelings, will often claim to be loved by their companion dogs and cats.)

178

There are numerous well-authenticated stories of animals risking their lives to save their loved ones. And animals will put their own safety second to protect their friends. One herd of elephants was seen always to travel unusually slowly. Observers noted that the herd travelled slowly so as not to leave behind an elephant who had not fully recovered from a broken leg. Another herd travelled slowly to accommodate a mother who was carrying her dead calf with her. When the herd stopped to eat or drink the mother would put her dead calf down. When they started travelling she would pick up the dead calf. The rest of the herd accommodated her in her time of grief. Gorillas, too, have been seen to travel slowly if one of their number is injured and unable to move quickly.

179

Try this simple questionnaire.

1. Do you like animals?
2. Do you agree animals suffer pain and distress if they are hurt or frightened?
3. Do you agree that if a kitten was ill it would be more sensible to treat it with a medicine which had been tested on other kittens than with a medicine which had been tested on cows?
4. Do you agree that medical treatments should be as free as possible from side effects?
5. Have you – or anyone you know – ever suffered an unpleasant side effect as a result of taking a drug?
6. Are you concerned about the number of side effects associated with modern drugs?
7. If you needed an operation would you rather the surgeon had experience of operating on other human beings rather than on cats, dogs or mice?
8. Do you agree that needless cruelty to animals should be stopped?
9. Would you be prepared to pay an extra few pence for drugs which you knew were less likely to cause serious side effects (or even kill you) because they had been properly tested rather than being tested on animals?
10. Did you know that there are no laws requiring drug or cosmetic companies to test their products on animals?
11. Would you be shocked to know that the animals used in laboratories include pets?
12. Do you agree that when people do things in your name – and with your money – you have a responsibility for what they do?

13. Did you realise that if new drugs were extensively and properly tested before being put onto the market many products would never be sold because they would be shown to be unsafe at an early stage?

14. Do you agree that animals should be treated with respect?

15. Do you agree that if animals are unlike human beings there is little point in using them to test drugs and procedures intended for human beings?

Now answer this final question:

What are you doing to help stop the use of animals in experiments?

180

Here are some quotes taken, at random, from research papers written by vivisectors:

♦ 'Holes were drilled in the cat's skull. The cat had a series of fits. The experimenters prefer to use former pets since these are more docile and easier to manage.'

♦ 'The two chimps were placed in a small metal container. After four weeks they became very depressed.'

♦ 'The cat's front legs were broken in a vice. The wounds were deliberately infected. The cat took four weeks to die.'

♦ 'The cat was fixed in an apparatus and a hole was made in its skull. A tube was placed in the hole and a series of chemicals poured down the tube, directly into the cat's brain. The cat remained conscious but was clearly irritated. It exhibited vocal signs of distress and struggled to escape.'

♦ 'The dogs were covered with an inflammable liquid. The liquid was then ignited. All the dogs suffered severe burns and died within a few days.'

♦ 'The cat was kept in a small cage and given daily injections of the drug being tested. After three months the cat had lost all its hair and had developed a serious skin condition. It became blind and lost control of its bowels. The cat was kept alive for three years and then the experiment was terminated.'

♦ 'Two days after the lamb was injected with the drug being tested it had a series of fits and vomited. It died shortly afterwards.'

♦ 'The cat was shot in the head. It died 90 minutes later.'

♦ 'The cat was force-fed with a household detergent until it died.'

♦ 'The chemical was dropped directly into the rabbit's eye. After 24 hours the eye had become red and clearly irritated. Within 48 hours the eye was opaque and suppurating and the animal was clearly in pain. After 72 hours the rabbit was blind.'

181

Animals frequently exhibit behaviour that can only be described as altruistic.

1. Old lionesses who have lost their teeth and can no longer bear young are, theoretically, of no value to the rest of the pride. But the younger lions will share their kills with them.

2. Young, agile chimpanzees will climb trees to fetch fruit for their older relatives.

3. Foxes have been observed bringing food to adult animals who are injured and unable to look after themselves. When one fox was injured by a mowing machine and taken to a vet, the fox's sister took food to the spot where her brother had lain. The good Samaritan sister fox made the whimpering sound that foxes use when summoning cubs to eat (even though she had no cubs).

4. Whales have been observed to ask for and receive help from other whales.

5. J. Howard Moore describes how crabs struggled for some time to turn over another crustacean which had fallen onto its back. When the crabs couldn't manage by themselves they went and fetched two other crabs to help them.

6. A gander who acted as a guardian to his blind partner would take her neck gently in his mouth and lead her to the water when she wanted to swim. Afterwards he would lead her home in the same manner. When goslings were hatched the gander, realising that the mother would not be able to cope, looked after them himself.

7. Pigs will rush to defend one of their group who is being attacked.

8. When wild geese are feeding one will act as sentinel – never taking a grain of corn while on duty. When the sentinel geese has been on watch for a while it pecks at a nearby goose and hands over the responsibility for guarding the group.

9. When swans dive there is usually one which stays above the water to watch out for danger.

10. Time and time again dogs have pined and died on being separated from their masters or mistresses.

11. Animals have even been known to give food to hungry humans. Koko, the gorilla who learned to communicate with humans through sign language, gave medical advice to a human woman who complained of indigestion. Koko told the woman to drink orange juice. When the human revisited ten days later and offered Koko a drink of orange juice, Koko would not accept the drink until assured that the woman felt better.

12. A Border collie woke a young mother from a deep sleep and led her to her baby's cot. The baby was choking on mucus and had stopped breathing. What is this but compassion? How can animal abusers regard themselves as sentient when they mistreat animals who can feel this way?

13. Konrad Lorenz described the behaviour of a gander called Ado when his mate Susanne-Elisabeth was killed by a fox. Ado stood by Susanne-Elisabeth's body in mourning. He hung his head and his body was hunched. He didn't bother to defend himself when attacked by strange geese. How would the animal abusers describe such behaviour other than as sorrow born of love? There is no survival value in mourning. It can only be a manifestation of a clear emotional response – love.

14. A badger was seen to drag another badger which had been killed by a car off the road, along a hedge, through a gap and into a burial spot in nearby woods.

15. Coyotes form pairs before they become sexually active – and then stay together. One observer watched a female coyote licking her partner's face after they had made love. They then curled up and went to sleep.

16. Geese, swans and mandarin ducks all enjoy long-term relationships. Animals can suffer, they can communicate and they can care.

182

Throughout human history those with power have punished others by putting them in cages or cells. Imprisonment takes away the individual's freedom and protects society from the individual. Anyone locked up will be considered (rightly or wrongly) to have committed a crime. Those considered to be most dangerous, or most deserving of punishment, will be kept in solitary confinement; locked alone in their cell, deprived of companionship.

Laboratory animals have committed no crimes but they are caged in the worst sort of comparable circumstances. They are kept, alone, in tiny cages (often little bigger than themselves) in a windowless room. Animals which would normally enjoy a vastly varied diet are denied access to their usual range of foods. They are fed dull, tasteless, food. They cannot create a nest or any other sort of real home. They cannot forage, burrow, climb, explore or enjoy the sun. They have no contact with other animals of their own or any other species. They cannot share their life with a partner. They are often housed in close proximity to equipment such as monitors and ventilation systems which produce ultrasonic sounds which cause them great distress. The only other thing they will hear will be the sound of other animals screaming in distress. Stressed to exhaustion they are constantly exposed to humans (a major cause of stress).

They are alone and frightened and the future offers only pain and more fear. The only release from their constant suffering will come through death.

183

Since the 1960's it has been known that rodent brains – like human brains – are stunted when they are deprived of mental stimulation. Stuck in a cage their behaviour changes.

Tens of millions of mice are housed in laboratories and half of them quickly develop repetitive behaviour patterns which have no function but which are a direct result of stress; they gnaw at their cage bars, run round and round in circles and pace to and fro. These actions, a direct result of their suffering, are repeated tens of thousands of times a day. The horrors of the experiments to which they will be exposed are merely added to their daily torment.

184

For more shocking truths about vivisection visit www.vernoncoleman.com

185

Much of the veterinary research done involving animals is designed not to find ways to improve the health of animals but to find ways to improve the profits made by farmers.

186

There is growing evidence to support the contention that many of today's new and most threatening viral epidemics have been generated by medical scientists working with animals. During the 1960's and 1970's cancer researchers and scientists working for the military on the development of death bugs were developing viruses in their laboratories. Researchers working for the military were using animals in their attempts to develop viral weapons with which opponents could be killed (and their countries destabilised) en masse.

Was it through incompetence (a common fault among the mass of second-rate scientists around the world who routinely perform experiments on animals) that new viruses have spread through our communities?

187

When debating the issue of vivisection many years ago (you can tell it was a long time ago because for a decade or so now vivisectors have refused to debate the issue with me in public) a leading supporter of animal experiments admitted that most animal experiments are misleading and provide false information if the results are extrapolated and applied to human patients. He admitted that he and his colleagues did not know which experiments might prove useful to doctors and which might be so misleading that they might actually be of negative benefit to doctors and patients.

I pointed out that if the experimenters themselves don't know which experiments are valid, and can be relied upon, then all experiments are useless. If you have 10 pieces of information and know that six of those pieces of information are inaccurate and that four are accurate – but don't know which six are bad and which four are good – then all 10 pieces of information are useless and aren't worth the effort of obtaining them.

Today, even the most enthusiastic vivisectors will admit that many of the experiments done on animals are grossly misleading and worthless. Moreover, they will also admit that they don't know which animal experiments are likely to produce accurate answers and which will produce misleading answers.

It still doesn't seem to have occurred to them that if you don't know which experiments are useful – and which are misleading – then all animal experiments are useless.

188

The World Medical Association's Declaration of Helsinki (on recommendations guiding physicians in biomedical research in human subjects) was officially amended in 2000, and laboratory procedures on animals are no longer recommended as essential before studies in humans are conducted.

189

The EU is testing 80,000 chemicals on animals because the chemical companies know they can't lose. If a test on an animal shows that a chemical causes cancer the test will be ignored on the grounds that animals and people are different. If a test on an animal shows that a chemical doesn't cause cancer in that animal the test will be used as proof that the chemical is safe. The EU is doing these tests because the chemical companies want them to do them. No one knows how many animals will die in entirely unnecessary tests but the final number will run into tens of millions.

Theoretically, the aim of all this death and destruction is to protect human beings from substances which cause cancer.

In reality, of course, neither the EU nor any individual government in Europe, cares about whether or not citizens develop cancer. If they did they would not have wilfully suppressed the evidence proving that eating meat is, with tobacco, the most important cause of cancer.

Incidentally, the tests being done by the EU are being duplicated by the American Government. This means, inevitably, that the number of animals dying quite pointlessly will, quite pointlessly, be doubled.

190

Primates living in the wild are killed so that hunters can capture their infants and sell them to vivisectors who are paid with money contributed by taxpayers.

191

In Britain, organisations which oppose vivisection are denied charitable status whereas charities (which claim all the tax benefits associated with charitable status) are allowed to campaign for vivisection.

What sort of world is it which gives special charitable status to organisations which abuse animals and yet denies charitable status to organisations which wants to save animals?

And you will probably be as astonished (and as horrified) as I am to discover that Britain's best known animal charity, the RSPCA, refuses to condemn all animal experiments. In fact, officially, the society still believes that some animal experiments are necessary.

I wrote to the RSPCA to protest about the fact that they refuse to condemn all barbaric torture of animals in laboratories and explained that evidence shows that animal experimentation is of no value. The RSPCA wrote back claiming that 'the weight of scientific opinion would appear to be against this.' I replied asking for the source of the 'weight of scientific opinion'.

I received no reply.

Those who support or defend animal experiments can never back up their opinion with evidence because there isn't any.

An RSPCA council member has told me that the RSPCA cannot condemn all animal experiments because, if it does so, it might lose its charitable status.

I wrote to all RSPCA Council members in an attempt to trigger a special meeting of some kind. But the silence has been deafening. The RSPCA, which exists to save animals, seems to me to be willing to sell its conscience (and the lives of millions of animals) for a substantial tax break (through charitable status).

If the RSPCA is allowing animals to be tortured and to die because it is frightened of losing a tax break then that is pitiful, pathetic and contemptible.

The organisation which decides which British organisations can claim charitable status (and which cannot) is the Charities Commission.

The Charities Commission is a Government department.

192

In the autumn of 1998, I began a guest appearance on a two hour long nationwide radio programme by challenging vivisectors and vivisectionists to name one disease for which a cure had been found through vivisection. Despite the fact that many vivisectionists telephoned the programme not one managed to come up with a disease for which vivisection had been an essential or integral part of the research process. I wasn't surprised. Vivisection is useless, always has been useless and always will be useless.

193

How could any sane, sentient being not feel disgusted by what goes on in animal research laboratories? There can surely be no moral or ethical justification for the legalised mayhem which, worldwide, results in the slow, painful destruction of around 1,000 dogs, cats, kittens, puppies, monkeys, rabbits and other animals every thirty seconds.

In Britain, where around 3 million experiments are performed every year, there is just a handful of inspectors to make sure that vivisectors obey what rules exist about animal treatment. The Home Office claims that the effectiveness of this tiny group of inspectors 'depends upon their ability to gain the respect and cooperation of the scientific community as, to function, inspectors must have unfettered access to the current and future plans of scientists'.

This seems as odd to me as a statement that the effectiveness of the police 'depends upon their ability to gain the respect and cooperation of the criminal community as, to function, policemen must have unfettered access to the current and future plans of criminals'.

194

Vivisectionists often claim that open-heart surgery wouldn't have developed without animal experiments.

This is yet another lie.

Open-heart surgery long pre-dates the often mistakenly credited animal experiments. In my book *The Story of Medicine* I reported that the first open-heart operation was performed by Professor Rehn of Frankfurt, who successfully repaired a right ventricular stab wound in 1896. In the scientific paper which announced the success of his operative procedure, Rehn explained that he was forced to operate by the fact that his patient was bleeding to death after being stabbed between the ribs with a kitchen knife. Just two years later (1898) doctors were proposing to operate on the mitral valve in order to restore cardiac function. These experiments were performed on real live human patients who would have died if surgery had not been attempted.

195

I disapprove of the actions of militant animal rights extremists for two reasons.

First, I don't believe that you can campaign to stop cruelty to one species by being cruel to another. Fighting for peace is the ultimate oxymoron. It's what George Bush and Tony Blair claim to do.

Second, those who use violence on behalf of animals are making a huge strategic error. Those of us who oppose vivisection have all the science on our side. Using violence merely gives the vivisectors and their supporters a chance to ignore the arguments against vivisection, an opportunity to portray anti-vivisectionists as violent nutters and an excuse to introduce endless new legislation which makes our society ever more repressive and which makes it increasingly difficult for anyone to speak out (let alone campaign) about anything.

But it's not difficult to understand the frustration of those who are outraged by the pointless and indefensible abuse of animals, who have been betrayed by politicians and who now feel utterly disenfranchised. Sadly, the extremism will, I predict, continue to get worse.

196

A private organisation called the Advertising Standards Authority exists in Britain, allegedly to protect consumers from dishonest advertisers. Although some people assume it is a statutory, official body the ASA isn't anything of the kind. It is a private organisation, financed mainly by large advertisers. And there are some who regard it as more concerned with protecting those sources of finance than the interests of consumers. As evidence that the ASA is out of touch with public opinion, commentators point to the fact that in one recent year the organisation took no action at all against the five advertisements which had caused the most offence to ordinary consumers. Five advertisements which had between them attracted more than 3,600 angry complaints were left untouched by the ASA. All these advertisements had been placed by large companies.

On the other hand, the ASA has consistently ruled against advertisements placed by anti-vivisectors – even though only one complaint may have been received. For example, when the Research Defence Society (an organisation set up and funded to defend vivisection) complained about two anti-vivisection leaflets of mine, the ASA quickly banned them. Amazingly, one of the people on the ASA committee which banned the leaflets was the vice chairman of L'Oreal (UK) Ltd, a large cosmetics company which has in the past been criticised by anti-vivisectors for its use of ingredients tested by means of animal experiments. The committee member also held an important position at the Cosmetics,

Toiletry and Perfumery Association. It is difficult to take the ASA seriously but newspapers and magazines do take notice of its judgements, and anti-vivisection campaigns have suffered as a result of the ASA's activities.

197

'I know not that by living dissections any discovery has been made by which a single malady is more easily cured.'
Dr Samuel Johnson

198

The power of the industry which supports, promotes and depends on vivisection is illustrated by the fact that anyone who opposes animal experiments (on whatever grounds) will quickly be labelled a 'lunatic' or, worse still, a terrorist. This is what is known as 'monstering' and the simple aim is to discredit and draw attention away from the message by discrediting the messenger. Because I have written and campaigned on behalf of animals (and, in particular, against vivisection), I have it on excellent authority that the authorities have been keeping an uncomfortably close eye on me for many years, and have tapped my telephones and dogged my footsteps, despite my frequently voiced disapproval of violence on both moral and practical grounds. The drug industry and the politicians who defend it have succeeded in whipping up the hysteria to such an extent that even the mildest form of anti-vivisection protest will be immediately stamped on as the work of militant crackpots. Read almost any national newspaper article on the subject, or watch any television programme on vivisection, and you will get the impression that those who oppose vivisection are hate-filled demons who want to see small children die of cancer. Newspaper editors and television producers would, it seems, give Al Queda a chance to defend itself before they would allow anti-vivisectionists to put forward reasoned arguments against the use of animal experiments.

199

Doing nothing isn't an option. If, now knowing what you know, you do nothing to stop this holocaust, you are just as guilty as those who take the animals, those who shutter the cages and those who wield the knives.

Millions prefer not to know what goes on in their names, and use their ignorance as an excuse for silence. Don't allow anyone you know to remain ignorant of the truth.

Vivisection is done in your name with your money. You have a right and a responsibility to speak out against it.

Every night, before you go to bed, ask yourself this simple question: 'What have I done today to help the animals and to help stop the evil practice of vivisection?'

Remember: once stopped, vivisection will never start again (it is so obviously unjustifiable on any terms). Our descendants will regard it as an evil practice and will be astonished that we allowed it to continue for as long as we did.

200

If you would like to help spread the truth about animal experiments, and help put an end to this vile practice, please encourage everyone you know to read this book.

The more people who know the truth, the more difficult it will be for the establishment to perpetuate the lie. Don't let your friends, colleagues, relatives or neighbours hide from the truth. It is harder to turn a blind eye when you know the truth.

Extra copies of this book are available from the publisher at specially subsidised prices.

The Author

Instinctively anti-authority and recklessly uncompromising, Vernon Coleman is the iconoclastic author of over 90 books which have sold over 2 million copies in the UK, been translated into 24 languages and now sell in over 50 countries. His best-selling non-fiction book *Bodypower* was voted one of the 100 most popular books of the 1980s/90s and was turned into two television series in the UK. The film of his novel *Mrs Caldicot's Cabbage War* was released early in 2003. In the 1980s, although several of his books had been high in the bestseller lists, he got fed up with nervous publishers trying to edit all the good bits out of his books and so he started his own publishing conglomerate which began life in a barn and now employs five people.

Vernon Coleman has written columns for *The Daily Star, Sun, Sunday Express, Planet on Sunday* and the *People* (resigning from the latter when the editor refused to publish a column questioning the morality and legality of invading Iraq) and has contributed over 5,000 articles, columns and reviews to 100 leading British publications including *Daily Telegraph, Sunday Telegraph, Guardian, Observer, Sunday Times, Daily Mail, Mail on Sunday, Daily Express, Woman, Woman's Own, Punch* and *Spectator*. His columns and articles have also appeared in hundreds of leading magazines and newspapers throughout the rest of the world. He edited the *British Clinical Journal* for one year until a drug company told the publisher to choose between firing him or getting no more advertising. For twenty years he wrote a column which was syndicated to over 40 leading regional newspapers. Eventually, the column had to be abandoned when Government-hired doctors offered to write alternative columns without charge to stop him telling readers the truth. In the UK he was the TV AM doctor on breakfast TV until he commented that fatty food had killed more people than Hitler. He was fired after a large food lobbyist had threatened to pull all its advertising. He was the first networked television Agony Aunt. In the past he has presented TV and radio programmes for both BBC and commercial channels though these days no producer who wants to keep his job for long is likely to invite him anywhere near a studio (especially a BBC studio). Many millions consulted his Telephone Doctor advice lines and visited his websites and for six years he wrote a monthly newsletter which had subscribers in 17 countries. Vernon Coleman has a medical degree, and an honorary science doctorate. He has worked for the Open University in the UK and was an honorary Professor of Holistic Medical Sciences at the Open International

University based in Sri Lanka. He used to give occasional lectures but these days the invitations are usually withdrawn when big companies find out about it. He has spoken about vivisection in the House of Commons and the House of Lords in London and has lectured doctors, nurses and other health professionals on the subject in a number of countries.

Vernon Coleman has received many really interesting awards from people he likes and respects. He is, for example, a Knight Commander of The Ecumenical Royal Medical Humanitarian Order of Saint John of Jerusalem, of the Knights of Malta and a member of the Ancient Royal Order of Physicians dedicated to His Majesty King Buddhadasa. In 2000 he was awarded the Yellow Emperor's Certificate of Excellence as Physician of the Millennium by the Medical Alternativa Institute. He is also Vice Chancellor of the Open International University. He has not been offered, and would not accept, any award by the British Government.

He worked as a GP for ten years (resigning from the NHS after being fined for refusing to divulge confidential information about his patients to State bureaucrats) and has organised numerous campaigns both for people and for animals.

He collects hobbies and accumulates books. He is a long-term member of the MCC. He has been intending to learn to speak French for over half a century but has made very little progress. He can ride a bicycle and swim, though not at the same time. He loves cats, cricket (before they started painting slogans on the grass), cycling, cafes and, most of all, the Welsh Princess.

Vernon Coleman is balding rapidly and is widely disliked by members of the Establishment. He doesn't give a toss about either of these facts. Many attempts have been made to ban his books but he insists he will keep writing them even if he has to write them out in longhand and sell them on street corners (though he hopes it doesn't come to this because he still has a doctor's handwriting). He is married to Donna Antoinette, the totally adorable Welsh Princess, and is very pleased about this. Together they have written two books *How To Conquer Health Problems Between Ages 50 And 120* and *Health Secrets Doctors Share With Their Families*.

Medical books by Vernon Coleman include:

The Medicine Men (1975)
Paper Doctors (1976)
Bodypower (1983)
Life Without Tranquillisers (1985)
The Story Of Medicine (1985, 1998)
Mindpower (1986)
The Health Scandal (1988)
The Twenty Minute Health Check (1989)
Mind over Body (1989)
How to Conquer Backache (1993)
How to Conquer Pain (1993)
Betrayal of Trust (1994)
Food for Thought (1994, revised edition 2000)
The Traditional Home Doctor (1994)
Relief from IBS (1995)
The Parent's Handbook (1995)
Power over Cancer (1996)
How to Conquer Arthritis (1996)
High Blood Pressure (1996)
How To Stop Your Doctor Killing You (1996, revised edition 2003)
Spiritpower (1997)
How To Relax and Overcome Stress (1999)
Superbody (1999)
Stomach Problems: Relief At Last (2001)
How To Overcome Guilt (2001)
How To Live Longer (2001)

with Donna Antoinette Coleman
How To Conquer Health Problems Between Ages 50 and 120 (2003)
Health Secrets Doctors Share With Their Families (2005)

Order from Publishing House • Trinity Place • Barnstaple •
Devon EX32 9HG • England
Telephone 01271 328892 • Fax 01271 328768
www.vernoncoleman.com

Animal rights books by Vernon Coleman

Animal Rights Human Wrongs

A passionate account of the political betrayal of animals (and animal lovers). Paperback £7.99

"I have already had the great pleasure of reading some of your books. The first one I obtained was Animal Rights – Human Wrongs. This is an astounding and very moving book. I pick it up and read it regularly." S.H., Devon

Why Animal Experiments Must Stop

Vernon Coleman analyses all the pro-vivisection arguments one by one – and destroys them. He shows how animal experiments endanger human health, and how they have been responsible for the deaths of thousands of people. Paperback £7.99

"I would like to add my voice to many who appreciate your work on behalf of animals." B.L., Eastbourne

Fighting For Animals

Complete action guide for animal lovers including winning strategies for defeating vivisection Paperback £7.99

Order from Publishing House • Trinity Place • Barnstaple • Devon EX32 9HG • England
Telephone 01271 328892 • Fax 01271 328768
www.vernoncoleman.com

Cat books by Vernon Coleman (1)

Alice's Diary

Thousands of delighted readers from around the world have bought this wonderful book which tells of a year in the life of a mixed tabby cat called Alice, who shares her life and her home with her two "Uprights". She records the year's events and disasters with great humour and insight and at long last gives us a glimpse of what it is really like to be a cat! Alice's Diary is delightfully illustrated throughout and is an absolute must for animal and cat lovers everywhere. £9.99 hardback

Alice's Adventures

After the publication of her hugely successful first book, Alice was inundated with fan mail urging her to put pen to paper once more. The result is this, her second volume of memoirs in which she shares with us yet another exciting and eventful year in her life. Illustrated. £9.99 hardback

Alice and Other Friends

Vernon Coleman's own account of life with Alice and her half sister Thomasina. The book is packed with stories, anecdotes and reminiscences about Alice and the many other creatures Vernon Coleman has met, known and lived with. Alice and Other Friends is liberally and beautifully illustrated with numerous line drawings by the author. £12.99 hardback

We Love Cats

We Love Cats is a real celebration of cats and is packed with humour and insight into the way cats think, behave and quietly run our lives. We Love Cats contains over 100 new and original Vernon Coleman drawings (he calls them catoons) plus poems, limericks and amazing facts about cats. £12.99 hardback

Order from Publishing House • Trinity Place • Barnstaple •
Devon EX32 9HG • England
Telephone 01271 328892 • Fax 01271 328768
www.vernoncoleman.com

Cat books by Vernon Coleman (2)

Cats' Own Annual

A chance to see the world through the eyes of some very literate cats. Packed with lists, poems, limericks and drawings. Contains cats' answers to the questions all Uprights ask. £12.99 hardback

The Secret Lives of Cats

The first time Uprights have ever been allowed access to the private correspondence exchanged by cats. The Secret Lives of Cats is full of wisdom and humour and will make you smile, cry and, at the end, feel warm all over. Illustrated by the author. £12.99 hardback

The Cat Basket

Vernon Coleman's biggest ever cat book, decorated by the author with an ample collection of his trademark catoons and packed with quizzes, anecdotes, amazing catfacts, stories and rhymes and love letters to cats. £12.99 hardback

Order from Publishing House • Trinity Place • Barnstaple •
Devon EX32 9HG • England
Telephone 01271 328892 • Fax 01271 328768
www.vernoncoleman.com

Political books by Vernon Coleman

England Our England (2002)

Rogue Nation (2003)

People Push Bottles Up Peaceniks (2003)

Confronting The Global Bully (2004)

Saving England (2004)

Why Everything Is Going To Get Worse Before It Gets Better (2004)

The Truth They Won't Tell You (And Don't Want You To Know) About The EU (2005)

Living in a Fascist Country (2006)

How To Protect and Preserve Your Freedom, Identity and Privacy (2006)

Order from Publishing House • Trinity Place • Barnstaple •
Devon EX32 9HG • England
Telephone 01271 328892 • Fax 01271 328768
www.vernoncoleman.com

Novels by Vernon Coleman

The Village Cricket Tour (1990)
The Bilbury Chronicles (1992)
Bilbury Grange (1993)
Mrs Caldicot's Cabbage War (1993)
Bilbury Revels (1994)
Deadline (1994)
The Man Who Inherited a Golf Course (1995)
Bilbury Pie (1995)
Bilbury Country (1996)
Second Innings (1999)
Around the Wicket (2000)
It's Never Too Late (2001)
Paris In My Springtime (2002)
Mrs Caldicot's Knickerbocker Glory (2003)
Too Many Clubs And Not Enough Balls (2005)
Tunnel (1980, 2005)

as Edward Vernon
Practice Makes Perfect (1977)
Practise What You Preach (1978)
Getting Into Practice (1979)

Order from Publishing House • Trinity Place • Barnstaple •
Devon EX32 9HG • England
Telephone 01271 328892 • Fax 01271 328768
www.vernoncoleman.com

What the readers say about
Vernon Coleman ...

"I write to let you know just what a profound effect your
three books *England Our England*, *Saving England*
and *Rogue Nation* have had on, I hope, not just myself."
R.H., GLOUCESTERSHIRE

"I have read with great interest your books *Rogue Nation* and
Confronting the Global Bully and admire your courage and
perception. My wife and I have also read (and put into practice)
the advice given in your books *How To Stop Your Doctor Killing
You*, *Food for Thought*, *Mindpower*, *Bodypower and Superbody*.
The results have been excellent, and we now enjoy far better
health than we have had for years."
MR S. S., CORTES ISLAND

"What a delightful, refreshing, practical and down-to-earth man
Dr Coleman is. I just love reading his books, whether on health
matters or stories or his views on politicians."
S.T., HAMPSHIRE

"I have read many of your books and borrowed some from
libraries though I found that was far from easy.
You have always made more sense to me than many of
the doctors who have treated me."
D.N., LONDON

"I have always looked forward to reading your views and so
agree with all you say. I only wish you could be Prime
Minister, maybe then we would get things right."
C.B., ESSEX

"Long may you continue to educate and enlighten us."
R.W., MIDDLESEX

"You are the voice for those of us who do not have access to the people who can make a difference." S.I., YORKSHIRE

"It's lovely to have someone who cares about people as you do. You tell us such a lot of things that we are afraid to ask our own doctors." K.C., NEWCASTLE

"I'm sure I'm not the only reader who derives great cheer from your incisive approach to politicians, professionals, business people and their inescapable spokespersons. More power to your elbow." J.W., FIFE

"Many people are now obliged to agree with things you have been saying for 30 years or more." J.F., BERKSHIRE

"I have purchased several of your books, which I have enjoyed immensely and found to be very informative and enlightening." L.G., SUSSEX

"We are most impressed with how clear and understandable the books are." P.B., RUGBY

"Your books really are marvellous." J. H., SOMERSET

"I just want to say how much I enjoy your books. I love the way you get your point across. I love the way you write. You are a literary genius...I am just about to order two more of your books on the internet. I'm really looking forward to reading them." C. C. DEVON

"Reading Dr Coleman's books I feel here is someone who has the courage to say and write what many people have felt about the way we are manipulated, brainwashed and controlled by large financial companies and the Government." J. J., DEVON